100 LITERACY HOMEWORK

RENEWED PRIMARY FRAMEWORK

100 LITERACY HOMEWORK ACTIVITIES

SCOTTISH PRIMARY 4

YEAR 3

◻ Credits

Author
Chris Webster

Updated by
Pam Dowson

Series consultant
Pam Dowson

Series editor
Tracy Kewley

Development editor
Rachel Mackinnon

Assistant editor
Gaynor Spry

Illustrations
Theresa Tibbetts/Beehive Illustration,
Garry Davies and Phil Garner

Book layout
Macmillan Publishing Solutions

Mixed Sources
Product group from well-managed
forests and other controlled sources
www.fsc.org Cert no. TT-COC-002769
© 1996 Forest Stewardship Council
FSC

Text © 2001, 2009, Chris Webster
Text © 2009, Pam Dowson
© 2009 Scholastic Ltd

Designed using Adobe InDesign

Published by Scholastic Ltd
Villiers House
Clarendon Avenue
Leamington Spa
Warwickshire CV32 5PR

www.scholastic.co.uk

Printed by Bell and Bain Ltd, Glasgow

1 2 3 4 5 6 7 8 9   9 0 1 2 3 4 5 6 7 8

British Library Cataloguing-in-Publication Data
A catalogue record for this book is available from the British Library.

ISBN 978-1407-10117-0

The rights of Chris Webster and Pam Dowson to be identified as the authors of this work have been asserted by them in accordance with the Copyright, Designs and Patents Act 1988.

Extracts from the Primary National Strategy's *Primary Framework for Literacy* (2006) http://nationalstrategies.standards.dcsf.gov.uk/primary/primaryframework/ © Crown copyright. Reproduced under the terms of the Click Use Licence.

Acknowledgements
The publishers gratefully acknowledge permission to reproduce the following copyright material:

Carlton Publishing Group for the use of 'Away from it all' by Ogden Nash from *Candy is Dandy: The Best of Ogden Nash with introduction by Anthony Burgess* © 1959, Ogden Nash (1994, Carlton Books Ltd). **David Higham Associates** for the use of the poem 'Little Spider' by Mervyn Peake from *A Book of Nonsense* by Mervyn Peake © 1972, Mervyn Peake (1972, Peter Owen). **Katherine Froman** for the use of 'Friendly Warning' by Robert Froman from *Seeing Things* by Robert Froman © 1974, Robert Froman (1974, Thomas Y Cromwell Co., New York). **Gerald Duckworth & Co Ltd** for the use of 'Overheard on a saltmarsh' by Harold Monro from *Collected Poems* by Harold Monro © 1970, Harold Monro (1970, Gerald Duckworth & Co Ltd). **Johnson and Alcock** for the use of an extract from *A Kind of Thief* by Vivien Alcock © 1991, Vivien Alcock (1991, Methuen Children's Books). **Laura Cecil Literary Agency** on behalf of the James Reeves Estate for the use of 'Moths and Moonshine' by James Reeves from *Complete Poems for Children* by James Reeves © 1994, James Reeves (1994, Heinemann). **OCLC PICA BV** for permission to base an article on the Dewey Decimal System © OCLC PICA BV. **Peters Fraser and Dunlop** for the use of 'I'm just going out for a moment' by Michael Rosen from *Wouldn't you like to know* by Michael Rosen © 1977, Michael Rosen (1977, Andre Deutsch) and for the use of 'Dialogue between two large village women' by James Berry from *Caribbean Poetry Now* edited by Stewart Brown © 1984, James Berry (1984, Arnold Overseas). **Rogers, Coleridge and White Ltd** for the use of an extract from *Storm* by Kevin Crossley-Holland © 1985, Kevin Crossley-Holland (1985, Heinemann Young Books). **Saltkrakan AB** for the use of an extract from *Emil gets into mischief* by Astrid Lindren © 1979, Astrid Lindgren (1979, Hamlyn). **Walker Books** for the use of 'Hot Sleepysaurus' by Martin Waddell from *Our Sleepysaurus* by Martin Waddell © 1998, Martin Waddell (1998, Walker Books).

Every effort has been made to trace copyright holders for the works reproduced in this book, and the publishers apologise for any inadvertent omissions.

CONTENTS

INTRODUCTION
100 Literacy Homework Activities: Year 3

About the series
The *100 Literacy Homework Activities* series provides easy-to-use, photocopiable homework sheets for Key Stage 1 and 2 children. Each book in the series contains 100 homework activities that can be embedded into any school homework programme. Each activity sheet provides instructions for the child and a brief note to the helper, stating simply and clearly its purpose and suggesting support and/or further challenge to offer the child. The activities are clearly linked to the renewed Primary Framework for Literacy and are organised by Block (Narrative, Non-fiction, Poetry), then by Unit.

Core skills activities
At the end of each Unit, you will find a number of 'Core skills' activities, designed to support the development of key literacy skills such as word recognition (Years 1 and 2 only), word structure and spelling, and sentence structure and punctuation. Some of the Core skills activities are linked to the content of the units; others are intended to be used for discrete teaching and can be used at any time.

Teachers' notes
The teachers' notes starting on page 8 provide further information about each activity, with notes on setting the homework, differentiation and follow-up work. The Narrative, Non-fiction and Poetry objectives on the teachers' notes show how activities are linked to the Unit plans, while the reference grid on pages 6 and 7 shows how the objectives from Strands 1 to 12 of the Framework are covered in the book. Links to the Scottish curriculum are provided on the Scholastic website (see page 7).

Using the resources
The best way to use these homework resources is to use them flexibly, integrating them with a series of literacy sessions over a number of days. At primary level, homework should be about 'consolidating and reinforcing skills and understanding, particularly in literacy and numeracy' (Department for Children, Schools and Families: Homework Guidelines). Although the homework sheets can be used to support assessment, their main purpose is to reinforce and extend literacy work carried out in class or to help children prepare for upcoming work.

Supporting your helpers
It is vital that parents or carers understand what you are trying to achieve with homework. As well as the 'Dear helper' notes on each sheet, there is a homework diary on page 5 which can be photocopied and sent home with the homework. Multiple copies of these can be fastened together to make a longer term homework record. Discuss with parents/carers what is meant by 'help'. Legitimate help will include sharing the reading of texts, helping to clarify problems, discussing possible answers and so on, but at some stage the child should be left to do his or her best. Tell parents/carers how much time you expect the child to spend on homework. If, after that time, a child is stuck, or has not finished, they should not be forced to continue. Ask parents/carers to write a brief explanation and say that you will give extra help the next day. If children are succeeding with a task and need more time, this can be allowed – but bear in mind that children need a varied and balanced home life!

Using the activities with *100 Literacy Framework Lessons*
Links have been provided on the teachers' notes for those who wish to use the homework activities with the corresponding *100 Literacy Framework Lessons* book. The teachers' notes show if and where a homework task might fit within the context of the appropriate *100 Literacy Framework Lessons* Unit.

www.scholastic.co.uk

📖 Homework diary

Name of activity and date sent home	Child's comments		Helper's comments	Teacher's comments
	Did you like this activity? Draw a face. 😊 😐 😞 a lot a little not much	How much did you learn? Draw a face. 😊 😐 😞 a lot a little not much		

Framework objectives

Objectives	Supporting activities (page numbers)
Strand 1: Speaking	
Choose and prepare poems or stories for performance, identifying appropriate expression, tone, volume and use of voices and other sounds.	35, 44, 71, 72, 76, 77, 114, 115, 116, 122, 124
Explain process or present information, ensuring items are clearly sequenced, relevant details are included and accounts are ended effectively.	42, 75, 84, 85, 88, 95, 96, 98
Sustain conversation, explain or give reasons for their views or choices.	28, 32, 33, 34, 37, 39, 41, 43, 49, 50, 52, 53, 61, 65, 71, 72, 74, 80, 81, 82, 83, 94, 102, 105, 106, 109, 110, 116, 118, 119, 120, 125
Develop and use specific vocabulary in different contexts.	31, 33, 34, 62, 70, 86, 95, 104, 107, 108, 127
Strand 2: Listening and responding	
Follow up others' points and show whether they agree or disagree in whole-class discussion.	
Identify the presentational features used to communicate the main points in a broadcast.	86
Identify key sections of an informative broadcast, noting how the language used signals changes or transitions in focus.	86
Strand 3: Group discussion and interaction	
Use talk to organise roles and action.	
Actively include and respond to all members of the group.	
Use the language of possibility to investigate and reflect on feelings, behaviour or relationships.	55
Strand 4: Drama	
Present events and characters through dialogue to engage the interest of an audience.	40, 44, 68, 69, 73, 74, 75
Use some drama strategies to explore stories or issues.	
Identify and discuss qualities of others' performances, including gesture, action and costume.	
Strand 6: Word structure and spelling	
Spell high and medium frequency words.	58, 66
Recognise a range of prefixes and suffixes, understanding how they modify meaning and spelling, and how they assist in decoding long, complex words.	46, 47, 59, 66, 67, 89, 90, 100, 101, 113, 121
Spell unfamiliar words using known conventions including phoneme-grapheme correspondences and morphological rules.	45, 46, 47, 59, 66, 67, 99, 100, 113, 121
Strand 7: Understanding and interpreting texts	
Identify and make notes on the main points of section(s) of text.	28, 42, 53, 54, 83, 84, 85, 86, 87, 91, 92, 93
Infer characters' feelings in fiction and consequences in logical explanations.	49, 50, 51, 52, 60, 65, 75

◗SCHOLASTIC
www.scholastic.co.uk

Framework objectives

Objectives	Supporting activities (page numbers)
Strand 7: Understanding and interpreting texts (cont.)	
Identify how different texts are organised, including reference texts, magazines and leaflets, on paper and on screen.	43, 62, 63, 73, 76, 80, 81, 82, 83, 88, 91, 92, 93, 94, 96, 102, 103, 104, 105, 106, 117, 118
Use syntax, context and word structure to build their store of vocabulary as they read for meaning.	28, 29, 37, 45, 55, 56, 70, 81, 84, 87, 88, 90
Explore how different texts appeal to readers using varied sentence structures and descriptive language.	48, 60, 76, 82, 119, 122, 123, 126
Strand 8: Engaging and responding to texts	
Share and compare reasons for reading preferences, extending the range of books read.	60, 61, 82
Empathise with characters and debate moral dilemmas portrayed in texts.	37, 39, 49, 50, 51, 71
Identify features that writers use to provoke readers' reactions.	29, 33, 51, 55, 60, 82, 84, 107, 117, 126
Strand 9: Creating and shaping texts	
Make decisions about form and purpose, identify success criteria and use them to evaluate their writing.	55, 64, 75, 97
Use beginning, middle and end to write narratives in which events are sequenced logically and conflicts resolved.	38, 40, 41, 43, 52, 53, 54, 55, 65, 74
Write non-narrative texts using structures of different text types.	48, 62, 64, 85, 88, 96, 97, 98, 108, 109, 110, 115, 120, 124, 125
Select and use a range of technical and descriptive vocabulary.	30, 31, 34, 56, 70, 76, 85
Use layout, format, graphics and illustrations for different purposes.	42, 62, 64, 97, 108, 117
Strand 10: Text structure and organisation	
Signal sequence, place and time to give coherence.	10, 30, 35, 41, 43, 56
Group related material into paragraphs.	56, 57, 63, 64, 65, 87, 110
Strand 11: Sentence structure and punctuation	
Show relationships of time, reason and cause through subordination and connectives.	58, 111, 112
Compose sentences using adjectives, verbs and nouns for precision, clarity and impact.	30, 55, 56, 64, 65, 115, 127
Clarify meaning through the use of exclamation marks and speech marks.	36, 56, 77, 78, 79
Strand 12: Presentation	
Write with consistency in size and proportion of letters and spacing within and between words, using the correct formation of handwriting joins.	63
Develop accuracy and speed when using keyboard skills to type, edit and redraft.	

Links to the Scottish curriculum can be found at www.scholastic.co.uk/literacyhomework/y3 (click on Free resources)

Narrative – Unit 1 Stories with familiar settings

Page 28 On the beach
Narrative objective: To engage in investigations and analysis of various settings.
Setting the homework: This activity should help the children to understand how to add detail to give more information about a setting. Tell the children that the author was trying to paint a picture of the setting with words, and as they read the passage, they should see what pictures come into their heads.
Back at school: Ask the children how successful they think the writer was in painting a word picture. Which parts were long shots and which were close ups? They could draw pictures of a selected part of the scene.
Link to *100 Literacy Framework Lessons Y3*: NU1, Phases 1 and 2: work on settings.

Page 29 Story settings
Narrative objective: To compare stories with familiar settings.
Setting the homework: Explain that writers cannot describe every detail in a scene; it would take up too much space, and would be boring. Instead, they select a few key details and describe them carefully. Ask the children to look for the key details of the scenes on the sheet. Tell them to underline or highlight the words and phrases that describe these details.
Back at school: Discuss each of the settings and share ideas about what brings each one to life. The children could choose a setting to use as the basis for a story.

Page 30 Picture the setting
Narrative objective: To write sentences to describe a setting.
Setting the homework: Ask the children to choose one of the picture settings and to describe it in detail, using the present tense, for example *The market place is filled with little stalls...* Encourage them to expand on the detail that can be seen in the pictures.
Differentiation: More confident learners could write about more than one picture.
Back at school: As a class, share the descriptions that the children have written. Ask the children to plan a story around the setting they have written about. A good way to begin the story is simply with the description of the setting, making only one change – putting it into the past (or 'storytelling') tense. For those children who chose to write about more than one setting, the others can be introduced later on in the story.
Link to *100 Literacy Framework Lessons Y3*: NU1, Phase 3, Day 1: exploring images of settings.

Page 31 What's most important?
Narrative objective: To discuss atmosphere and common features and themes of settings.
Setting the homework: You should work through an example of a 'zones of relevance' board with the class, explaining that the most important words go in the centre circle, less important in the next two circles. Give the children a theme to use, linked to your current focus.
Differentiation: Less confident learners could put just one or two words in each circle, more experienced could aim higher.
Back at school: Share results – how many children have selected the same words, and did they put them in the same parts of the diagram?
Link to *100 Literacy Framework Lessons Y3*: NU1, Phase 3: work on settings.

Page 32 In the kitchen
Narrative objective: To engage in investigations and analysis of various settings.
Setting the homework: Using a different setting as the context, ask the children to use their senses to describe what they would experience. This homework could be linked to 'A Pudding Like a Night on the Sea' from Ann Cameron's *Julian Stories*.
Differentiation: You could give children with different levels of experience a different minimum number of words to write for each box.
Back at school: Compare the children's lists. Has anyone spotted something that others missed? Is there anything they would like to add to the setting?
Link to *100 Literacy Framework Lessons Y3*: NU1, Phases 1 and 3: work on settings.

Page 33 Settings on screen
Narrative objective: To engage in investigations and analysis of various settings; to discuss atmosphere and common features and themes.
Setting the homework: This is intended to be used as a follow-up to work from Phase 1 of the Unit, on aspects of visual elements used in film. The children must already have an understanding of the technical terms involved, such as *camera angle* and so on. You could ask them to suggest possible TV programmes from those currently available.
Differentiation: Less confident learners could be asked to focus on one or two of the elements, rather than attempting all four.
Back at school: Compare results. Are there similarities between live action and animated programmes?

Page 34 Creating an atmosphere
Narrative objective: To investigate and write sentences through modelled and shared composition.
Setting the homework: You should have done some work on comparing the atmosphere in settings, or changing the atmosphere in a text by changing the language. Tell the children to use their senses when writing about each setting.
Differentiation: Less confident learners could write one or two words rather than sentences, or be asked to complete a limited number of boxes on the sheet.
Back at school: Ask children to read their words, phrases or sentences to a partner, who has to work out which setting is being described. Discuss differences in language used.
Link to *100 Literacy Framework Lessons Y3*: NU1, Phases 1 and 3: work on atmosphere.

Page 35 How commas help – Core skills
Objective: To identify commas and understand how they affect a passage of text.
Setting the homework: Remind the children of some of the main uses of commas. When reading aloud, a comma usually indicates a slight pause. Explain to the children that they should prepare the text by highlighting the commas and then should read it aloud to someone. After the reading, they should discuss how the commas helped their reading.
Back at school: Move on to more specific uses of the comma and/or other punctuation marks that help the reader.

Page 36 Punctuation pointers – Core skills
Objective: To understand the need for punctuation.
Setting the homework: Explain that, for the homework to work properly, the two passages must be read aloud.
Differentiation: Only children who have progressed to the appropriate stage should be asked to do the second part of the second task.
Back at school: Discuss why the lack of punctuation made reading the passages difficult. Display the passages and invite children to add the correct punctuation.

Narrative – Unit 2 Myths, legends, fables, traditional tales

Page 37 Theseus and the Minotaur
Narrative objective: To describe the key characters in a quest myth.
Setting the homework: It will help if you have already done some work on quest myths, particularly those where monsters feature, such as Odysseus and the Cyclops or Beowulf and Grendel. Tell the children to use their imagination as well as the information in the text when completing the activity.
Differentiation: Less confident learners could just draw the picture.
Back at school: Let the children compare their drawings and written responses. Ask some to read Theseus' thoughts, in role, with appropriate emphasis and intonation.
Link to *100 Literacy Framework Lessons Y3*: NU2, Phase 1: work on monsters and heroes.

Page 38 Typical story language

Narrative objective: To investigate language features in a traditional story.

Setting the homework: Explain to the children that an important feature of traditional tales is the language in which they are written. This language reflects the fact that the stories were usually passed on by word of mouth for hundreds of years. Encourage the children to relate the example phrases to stories they have read and to think of or collect more examples and add them to the list. They should then try to use some of the words and phrases in a story of their own.

Differentiation: Less confident learners could limit their work to writing examples rather than tackling their own story.

Back at school: Share examples of traditional story language and some of the stories.

Page 39 The choosing

Narrative objective: To identify and discuss common themes in a traditional story.

Setting the homework: The children should be familiar with the term 'theme', although you may wish to revise it: a theme is a main idea expressed in a story (for example, the triumph of good over evil), as opposed to plot, which is what happens in the story.

Differentiation: Theme is an abstract concept which less confident learners will probably not be able to grasp at this stage. However, they can enjoy and discuss the story at a more concrete level, and should be able to answer the questions.

Back at school: Discuss the answers to the questions. Ask the children to share any situations they have experienced where they had to make choices. Read a number of other short fairy and folk tales and try to identify the themes.

Page 40 Quest myth plan

Narrative objective: To use oral storytelling to plan a quest myth.

Setting the homework: Explain how to use the cards to provide a basic framework for planning a quest myth which the children should then tell someone at home. They can select the cards to ensure there is one from each category, but the story must be in a sensible sequence.

Differentiation: More confident learners could use more than one element for a section, or add elements of their own.

Back at school: Children take turns to tell their favourite story to a partner.

Link to *100 Literacy Framework Lessons Y3*: NU2, Phase 1: creating a quest myth.

Page 41 Plot cards

Narrative objective: To plan and write own stories.

Setting the homework: Explain that many fairy tales are developed from a small number of basic plots, six of which are given on the sheet. Ask the children to discuss these plots with their helpers and to elaborate them by adding other ideas. Finally, they should choose one to write into a detailed story plan.

Differentiation: Less confident learners can follow the plots in a straightforward way. More confident learners should be encouraged to elaborate the plots and/or borrow from other plots.

Back at school: Share and discuss story plots, then begin the first draft of the stories.

Page 42 Story game

Narrative objective: To sequence key events in a story.

Setting the homework: The children will need to take a copy of the story from page 41 'Plot cards' home. If this is not possible, provide a summary sheet for them to work from. Make sure that the story lends itself to this kind of treatment. Most stories with a linear plot will work well. If possible, show the children a 'worked example'. This could be a good example from another class, or one you have prepared yourself. It is a good idea to enlarge the homework sheet to A3.

Differentiation: More confident learners could be encouraged to elaborate on the basic idea by adding in ideas from other board games they know about, for example 'Chance' cards.

Back at school: Share and discuss the games. The children will enjoy playing each other's games. If different groups of children have written about different books, the games may well stimulate an interest in further reading.

Page 43 How the elephant got a long trunk
Narrative objective: To plan and write stories in the style of a myth.
Setting the homework: Remind the children that myths often try to explain something we don't understand or how something came to be. Explain to the children that they should use the myth on the sheet, which explains how elephants got their long trunks, as a model for a similar myth of their own. Some ideas are given at the bottom of the page to help them, but they should be encouraged to come up with their own ideas if appropriate.
Back at school: Discuss the myth of the elephant's trunk. Ask: *Is it a good explanation? Why did people long ago make up such myths?* Share the myths the children have written.

Page 44 The sequel game
Narrative objective: To plan and write stories in the style of a myth.
Setting the homework: Define the term 'sequel': a follow-on story that uses some of the same characters and settings. Ensure that the children are familiar with the basic stories featured on the sheet. Adapt the sheet, if necessary, to include more familiar titles.
Differentiation: The only obstacle to planning a sequel is lack of knowledge of the characters and settings of the original. Ensure that all the children are able to participate by adapting the sheet appropriately.
Back at school: Share plans for the sequels. These could then be written up and edited into a class book of traditional-story sequels.

Page 45 A pair of trousers – Core skills
Objective: To understand the terms 'singular' and 'plural'.
Setting the homework: Revise the terms 'singular' and 'plural' and think of some examples in class.
Back at school: Go over the exercise, particularly the more difficult words, for example, *a pair of shoes* – two objects, but the word *pair* makes them grammatically singular; *sheep* and *fish* – the same in both singular and plural so should appear in both columns; *trousers* – one object, but grammatically plural; the addition of *a pair of* would make it singular; *flock* – a collective noun; it refers to a group of animals, but is grammatically singular.

Page 46 Multi-purpose prefixes – Core skills
Objective: To use prefixes to create new words.
Setting the homework: Explain that many prefixes are linked to particular words and cannot be used flexibly. For example, we say *unhappy* and *disagree*, but it is wrong to say *dishappy* and *unagree*. However, there are some prefixes which can be used very flexibly to create new words, and indeed, many recent new words have been formed from them, for example *supermarket*. Go over the three examples on the homework sheet with the children. Encourage them to combine one of the prefixes with any word they can think of, then to say what their new word means. For example, 'cyber-' + 'desk' = *cyberdesk: a special desk with a built-in computer.*
Back at school: Enjoy sharing the new words and definitions. Create a class dictionary of them. Research the use of these prefixes in the real world, for example *megastore*. Ask the class to write a story set in the future using as many of the new words as possible.

Page 47 Multi-purpose suffixes – Core skills
Objective: To use suffixes to create new words.
Setting the homework: Explain that many suffixes are linked to particular words and cannot be used flexibly. For example, we say *beautiful* but not *happiful*. However, there are some suffixes which can be used very flexibly to create new words, for example *readathon*, which uses the suffix '-athon', from *marathon*, meaning a long event requiring lots of stamina. Ten of the most common of these multi-purpose suffixes are listed on the homework sheet. Go over the three examples with the children and encourage them to combine the suffixes with any word they can think of, then to say what it means, for example *gorilla-speak – a special language made up of grunts.*
Back at school: Create a class dictionary of new words. Research the use of these suffixes in the real world, for example *user-friendly*.

Narrative – Unit 3 Adventure and mystery

Page 48 Will-o'-the-wykes and bogles
Narrative objective: To analyse language use in a story.
Setting the homework: Explain that part of our enjoyment of a story is in the build-up and atmosphere as much as in the events themselves.
Differentiation: Less confident learners should focus on more basic points of literature study such as plot and character.
Back at school: Talk about definitions of the atmosphere created – anything in the 'spooky' or 'frightening' line will do. Discuss which words and phrases were highlighted. Debate what might happen next. The children can write the next scene.

Page 49 Pirates
Narrative objective: To discuss characters' feelings and relationships.
Setting the homework: Explain that both texts give us clues about the characters' feelings and relationships. Children should first study the basic character description, then look for evidence for the characters' feelings and relationships.
Differentiation: You may wish to ask less confident learners to omit the highlighting of adjectives exercise.
Back at school: Discuss the two characters. Long John's appearance is rough and forbidding, but at this point in the story he appears to be a kindly, cheerful person. Captain Hook comes across as a cruel man who dominates others by fear.

Page 50 Emil
Narrative objective: To discuss characters' feelings and behaviour.
Setting the homework: Explain to the children that this extract introduces us to Emil. In order to get enough information for a full character study we would have to find out what he does and how he changes throughout the story.
Back at school: Discuss the children's answers. The third question could be used as a basis for the children to write their own adventures for Emil.
Link to *100 Literacy Framework Lessons Y3*: NU3, Phase 1, Day 2: characters.

Page 51 Character card
Narrative objective: To discuss characters' feelings and behaviour.
Setting the homework: Ask the children to use the template (enlarged to A3 if possible) to write about one of the main characters in a story that has been read and studied in class. Note that they will need to take the text home with them. If this is not possible, provide them with a written summary of the text and some notes and quotes – or get the children to do this in a lesson.
Differentiation: More confident learners should be encouraged to write more extensive portraits.
Back at school: Share ideas about the main characters.
Link to *100 Literacy Framework Lessons Y3*: NU3, Phase 1, Day 2: characters.

Page 52 Layla's adventure
Narrative objective: To write a recount of an incident from a story in the form of a letter.
Setting the homework: Children will need to know the basic format of writing a letter before doing this activity. Explain that they will be writing in role, so will need to imagine the character's thoughts and feelings, and how they would explain these to a close friend. Remind them about using the first person.
Back at school: Children read their letters to a partner before feeding back to the class the similarities and differences between their letters.
Link to *100 Literacy Framework Lessons Y3*: NU3, Phase 2, Days 3 to 5: recounting a character's feelings.

Page 53 Once upon a time
Narrative objective: To analyse language use in a story.
Setting the homework: Ask the children to talk about each of the openings with their helper with a particular focus on what kind of story each opening might lead in to.
Differentiation: Less confident learners could concentrate on the first task only.
Back at school: Discuss the openings, then ask the children to choose one to develop into a story during shared or guided writing.

Page 54 Happily ever after
Narrative objective: To analyse language use in a story.
Setting the homework: Ask the children to talk about each of the endings with their helper, with a particular focus on what kind of story might have led up to them.
Differentiation: Less confident learners could concentrate on the first task only.
Back at school: Discuss the endings, then ask the children to choose one and write a story to go with it during shared or guided writing. Alternatively, the children could cut up the openings from page 53 and the endings from page 54, shuffle them and then try to match them up. More confident learners could combine them at random, and try to write a story that fits.

Page 55 Cliffhangers
Narrative objective: To investigate the plot structure of a longer adventure or mystery story.
Setting the homework: This activity will help the children when they are planning to write a longer story which has a sequence of events, perhaps divided into short chapters. Ensure they understand the term 'cliffhangers' – relate it to TV serials, such as *Doctor Who*, or others they may know.
Differentiation: Less confident writers can add one sentence, while others can choose one cliffhanger to write an extended piece on the reverse of the sheet.
Back at school: In small groups, children share their work, for others to give positive comments.
Link to *100 Literacy Framework Lessons Y3*: NU3, Phase 1, Day 6: work on cliffhangers.

Page 56 Improve a story
Narrative objective: To plan and write an extended adventure story.
Setting the homework: Explain how stories can be improved by including more detail. For example, the short description of Pegleg could be compared with the description of Captain Hook on page 49. Ask the children to plan some more adventures for Pegleg.
Back at school: Compare ways of improving the story. Share ideas for additional adventures. The children could then either write the full-length story of Pegleg the pirate in chapters, or apply the skill to another topic.

Page 57 Puppy problem – Core skills
Objective: To use paragraphs in story writing.
Setting the homework: Explain the basic rules of paragraphing (begin a new paragraph for each big step forward in the story; leave a space between paragraphs). Explain that the template on the homework sheet will help the children to apply these rules.
Differentiation: More confident learners should be encouraged to develop the template and write a longer story with more paragraphs.
Back at school: Encourage the children to apply the rules of paragraphing without the support of a template. This can be done in stages, for example by first suggesting a paragraph plan and leaving the children to set out the paragraphs correctly and then leaving them to work out their own paragraph plans.

Page 58 Combine sentences – Core skills
Objective: To use connectives to form compound sentences.
Setting the homework: Revise the term 'connective' – a connective is a joining word.
Differentiation: All the children should be able to do this homework even if they do not understand the term 'connective'.
Back at school: Discuss the connectives the children used – in many cases, a number of equally correct answers are possible.

Page 59 Non-stick – Core skills
Objective: To recognise and spell the prefixes 'non-', 'ex-', 'co-' and 'anti-'.
Setting the homework: Note that the prefixes 'non-', 'ex-', 'co-' and 'anti-' have been chosen (using only one meaning of 'ex-': *former*) as these are the prefixes most often used to coin new words.
Back at school: Share the new words. An interesting follow-up would be to ask children to sketch their new product (for example, an anti-tangle shampoo) and write an advertisement or instruction manual for it.

Narrative – Unit 4 Authors and letters

Page 60 Book review
Narrative objective: To write a book review.
Setting the homework: This sheet can be given to children when they finish their individual reading books. Early in the term, it is worth going over the writing frame on the sheet with all the children. Explain that the phrases and the paragraph layout act as a 'skeleton' for a book review.
Back at school: It is a good idea to have a class folder for book reviews. When children have written a book review, and you have read it, it can be placed in the folder for other children to read.
Link to *100 Literacy Framework Lessons Y3*: NU4, Phase 1, Day 5: writing a book review.

Page 61 Author hunt
Narrative objective: To find out about an author, and express personal responses about their work.
Differentiation: More confident readers can be allowed to choose authors of their own, while others may need greater direction.
Back at school: Children can read some of their information, for others to work out who the author is. The information could be used to create a display.
Link to *100 Literacy Framework Lessons Y3*: NU4, Phase 1: learning about an author.

Page 62 Dick King-Smith
Narrative objective: To present information about an author in an on-screen format.
Setting the homework: Look at some author websites and talk about how the information is arranged on the page. Look at features such as headings and hyperlinks, different font choices and what kinds of illustrations are included. Demonstrate how to annotate a piece of text similar to that on the homework sheet.
Differentiation: Consider providing print outs of a web page for children who you know do not have internet access at home.
Back at school: Use ICT sessions for children to create their redesigned web page using the 'web wizard' facility of a software program.
Link to *100 Literacy Framework Lessons Y3*: NU4, Phase 1: learning about an author.

Page 63 Letters
Narrative objective: To use the conventions of letter writing including paragraph organisation.
Setting the homework: Before giving out the sheet, revise the points given in the guidelines at the top of the page. If children have access to a computer at home, they could be encouraged to word-process their letter.
Differentiation: Note that this homework focuses on the first steps of paragraphing; it is therefore not suitable for more confident learners. They could be asked to write a letter from scratch using clear paragraphs. Help less confident learners by suggesting that the letter will divide neatly into three paragraphs.
Back at school: Check how well the children have applied the skill to their own personal letter, where appropriate. Where necessary, provide reinforcement of the skill.
Link to *100 Literacy Framework Lessons Y3*: NU4, Phases 2 and 3: writing letters.

■SCHOLASTIC
www.scholastic.co.uk

Page 64 Letter to an author
Narrative objective: To plan and write a letter to an author.
Setting the homework: Explain that the writing frame is only a guide. Encourage the children to write what they really want to say. The writing frame gives good ways of starting and ending a letter, but the children could use their own thoughts for the middle.
Differentiation: Less confident learners should follow the writing frame closely.
Back at school: Discuss the drafts of the letters, redraft them to make them as good as possible. Rather than bombarding an author or their publisher with letters, the class could pool their ideas in a whole-class letter to one chosen author and send that.
Link to *100 Literacy Framework Lessons Y3*: NU4, Phases 2 and 3: writing letters.

Page 65 Letter to a character
Narrative objective: To write letters for a specific audience and purpose.
Setting the homework: The children should already have had some experience at writing informal letters before doing this activity. You may wish to suggest particular books for them to choose their character from – perhaps one you have been working on together, or one they have read in guided reading.
Differentiation: You could provide sentence prompts for less confident learners.
Back at school: The letters can be swapped with other children who are familiar with the character, for them to write a reply in role, or some examples read out to the class.
Link to *100 Literacy Framework Lessons Y3*: NU4, Phases 2 and 3: work on letters.

Page 66 Prefix game – Core skills
Objective: To understand how prefixes change meaning.
Setting the homework: Define 'prefix': a word-part added to the beginning of a word to change its meaning. Explain how to play the prefix game using the instructions on the homework sheet.
Differentiation: Ask more confident learners to think about how prefixes change the meanings of words.
Back at school: Write the correct matches of prefixes and words on the board in discussion with children. Talk about how the prefixes change the meanings of the words.

Page 67 Where's my partner? – Core skills
Objective: To explore gender suffixes.
Setting the homework: Explain the task. Encourage the children to seek the support of their helper for the second task.
Differentiation: Less confident learners could do the first task only.
Back at school: Quickly go over the matching exercise, then explore which feminine forms are little used today. Discuss reasons for this.

Narrative – Unit 5 Dialogue and plays

Page 68 Finger puppets
Narrative objective: To use known stories as a basis for improvised dialogue.
Setting the homework: Show the children how to make the very simple cylinder puppets, which slide on the finger, and demonstrate how they can be used in a short scene from a well-known story. You could use a traditional tale, or characters from a story you are currently sharing.
Back at school: Children can share their finger puppets and enjoy acting out their scenes. Characters from different stories can be put together to see what might happen! Good examples can be performed for the rest of the class.
Link to *100 Literacy Framework Lessons Y3*: NU5, Phase 1: work on dialogue.

Page 69 How should I say that?
Narrative objective: To choose descriptive words for stage directions.
Setting the homework: Ensure the children know what stage directions are, and that in this case they are describing how someone speaks. Tell the children that most of the words on the sheet are adverbs – the ones that end in 'ly'. Briefly collect a list of adverbs that could describe how people might say something.
Differentiation: You may wish to provide less confident readers with a list of suggested adverbs from which to choose.
Back at school: Pairs of children can compare their adverb choices, practise and perform their playscripts for others to guess what adverbs they chose.
Link to *100 Literacy Framework Lessons Y3*: NU5, Phases 2 and 3: adding stage directions.

Page 70 Play language
Narrative objective: To learn some of the technical vocabulary associated with plays and playscripts.
Setting the homework: The children will need to have done some work on the conventions of playscripts before doing this activity. Tell them to start with the words and definitions they already know before working out those they are less familiar with. Using different coloured pencils to draw the lines makes it much easier to check answers.
Back at school: Check the answers together as a class, with children checking their own work. As a follow-up, the children could look for examples of the words in playscripts.
Link to *100 Literacy Framework Lessons Y3*: NU5, Phase 2: work on playscript conventions.

Page 71 Schoolbot
Narrative objective: To perform playscripts.
Setting the homework: Explain to the children that this scene sets up a situation that could be developed into a play. Spend a few moments going over the conventions of drama scripts: scene descriptions in present tense, brief directions in brackets, no speech marks for dialogue and no reporting clauses (for example, *said Schoolbot*).
Back at school: Organise the children into groups of four to six. In each group, one child should play the part of the teacher, one Schoolbot, and the others should play the children in the class. Ask the groups to begin by reading the script, then to improvise more scenes. Emphasise that they need to make up names for the characters of the children and to give each one a worthwhile part to play. The lesson might conclude with one or two of the groups acting out a scene from their play to the rest of the class.

Page 72 All in good time
Narrative objective: To write and perform playscripts.
Setting the homework: Ask children to read the play with their helper first and then discuss how it could be prepared for performance. Ask them to think about the following: casting, staging, props, acting, movement.
Differentiation: Less confident learners need not write the extra scene. They could think of an idea.
Back at school: Discuss ideas for the performance and for extra scenes, and ask for volunteers to read out examples. Transfer the skills to another, longer play, or extend the playscript by adding some of the best extra scenes.

Page 73 Scripting Cinderella
Narrative objective: To identify features of narrative that support the writing of playscripts.
Setting the homework: Children will need to have read some playscripts before doing this activity. Tell them to use their knowledge of speech marks to help in finding the spoken words that would re-appear as lines in a script, and to look for adverbs or other words that can be used for stage directions.
Differentiation: Less confident learners could just look for the dialogue.
Back at school: Pairs of children can compare their results. An extension activity would be to actually write the scene as a playscript, and perhaps act it out.

Page 74 Planning a playscript
Narrative objective: To plan playscripts based on familiar stories.
Setting the homework: Go through the sections that will need to be planned to ensure the children understand the task. You may wish to give them all the same story and/or scene to work from, or let them choose their own – using a traditional tale works well.
Back at school: Pairs of children can share their plans, giving each other feedback. The next step is for the plans to be used as the basis for actually writing the scene, which can later be rehearsed and performed.
Link to *100 Literacy Framework Lessons Y3*: NU5, Phase 2: planning a playscript.

Page 75 Bored boy
Narrative objective: To write playscripts based on a story.
Setting the homework: Spend a few moments going over the conventions of drama scripts. Ask the children to compare the story text with the playscript 'starter' at the bottom of the page.
Differentiation: More confident learners should be able to complete the playscript. Less confident learners could just compare the two versions of the story.
Back at school: The children should apply the skill to writing an extended drama script. Ask each group to write a script of their improvised drama. If the subject matter of the drama was planned in advance, each scene could be edited together to form a full-length play. Try to find a performance opportunity for the play, for example, in an assembly.

Page 76 Mash – Core skills
Objective: To use synonyms for *said*.
Setting the homework: Remind the children that dialogue can be brought to life by using synonyms of *said*. This gives the text variety and tells us more about the feelings of the speaker. This is not a one-for-one cloze procedure: there are more synonyms than gaps, and synonyms can be used twice.
Differentiation: More confident learners can think of synonyms of their own.
Back at school: Discuss the most effective synonym for each gap. Get the children to apply the skill to their own story-writing.

Page 77 Hot Sleepysaurus – Core skills
Objective: To identify speech marks.
Setting the homework: Revise speech marks with the children. It is worth pointing out that speech marks can occur as single or double quote marks. Emphasise that they are used before and after words actually spoken.
Differentiation: Identifying speech marks is one of the first steps in learning to punctuate dialogue. This homework is therefore most suited to less confident learners.
Back at school: Ask for a small group of volunteers to share reading the passage aloud. To do this well, they will have to take account of the speech marks.

Page 78 Capital letters in speech – Core skills
Objective: To use capital letters appropriately in speech.
Setting the homework: Remind the children of the uses of capital letters that they have covered so far, such as for the personal pronoun 'I', at the start of a sentence, for the names of people and places and for headings and titles. Revise the use of capital letters in dialogue by using the explanation on the sheet.
Differentiation: This skill should be introduced when a child has both mastered the basic uses of capital letters and learned how to use speech marks. Less confident learners who have not mastered these skills should be given work on these instead.
Back at school: Display an enlarged copy of the sheet and revise the uses of capital letters. As a follow up, ask the children to write a story with dialogue.

Page 79 Willa's baby – Core skills
Objective: To identify and use appropriate punctuation in speech.
Setting the homework: Explain that the highlighting exercise focuses attention on the punctuation. This will then be used as a model for their own writing.
Differentiation: Less confident learners should focus on one aspect of speech punctuation at a time.
Back at school: Give the children opportunities to apply the skill to the context of writing dialogue for stories.

Non-fiction – Unit 1 Reports

Page 80 Fiction and non-fiction
Non-fiction objective: To revise the differences between fact and fiction.
Setting the homework: Ensure that the children understand the terms: 'fiction' – a made-up story (a true story is usually biography or history); 'non-fiction' – any type of writing that is not a story (for example, history, science, diaries, advertisements, reports); and 'fact' – something that is true.
Differentiation: This sheet is a simpler alternative to page 81, 'Fact or fiction?'. Both sheets can be used at the same time, with less confident learners using this sheet and the more confident learners using page 81.
Back at school: Discuss the sorting exercise, particularly how the children classified Operation Titanic and The Story of Queen Victoria. A good follow-up would be a visit to the library to see how books are classified.

Page 81 Fact or fiction?
Non-fiction objective: To revise the differences between fact and fiction.
Setting the homework: Ensure that the children understand the terms 'fiction', 'non-fiction' and 'fact' (see above). Explain that the task is to sort the openings into fact and fiction. Some are easy, but others are intended to be thought-provoking. For example, the last one sounds like a fact, but does Fushun really exist?
Differentiation: This sheet is a more difficult alternative to page 80, 'Fiction and non-fiction'. Both sheets can be used at the same time, with less confident learners using page 80 and the more confident learners using this sheet.
Back at school: Discuss the sorting exercise, with a particular focus on the thought-provoking lines. Some of the points to bring out are:
- A text can sound factual because of the way it is written, but could be deliberately false or could be fiction.
- A story can be written about a factual event. Is it then fact or fiction? The answer depends on the style in which it is written and who it is written for.
- It is difficult to classify texts about people's beliefs (for example, belief in God, belief in Atlantis) as fact or fiction. This is where the term non-fiction is so helpful.

Page 82 Crocodiles
Non-fiction objective: To revise the differences between fact and fiction.
Setting the homework: Revise the terms 'fiction' and 'non-fiction' (see above). Explain that the extracts on the sheet are very short, but that there is just enough text to be able to answer the questions. Ask the children to discuss the questions with their helper and to write their answers on the back of the page.
Differentiation: For less confident learners, the sheet could be simplified by deleting the 'Fiction' and 'Non-fiction' headings and the questions. The children could then be asked to say which passage is fiction and which is non-fiction.
Back at school: Discuss the questions at the bottom of the sheet. Find and compare other examples of fiction and non-fiction passages on the same subject.

Page 83 Arctic challenge
Non-fiction objectives: To learn how to locate information in a text.
Setting the homework: Explain the task to the children, telling them that they only write down the chapter headings, the page numbers are not needed. Tell them to do the ones they find easiest first, and make good guesses at the ones they are less sure of.
Differentiation: More confident readers could use other sources to find real information about some of the topics.
Back at school: Display the answers for children to check their own work. Ask some children to explain how they worked out the more difficult questions.
Link to *100 Literacy Framework Lessons Y3*: NFU1, Phase 3: locating information.

◼ SCHOLASTIC
www.scholastic.co.uk

Page 84 Hurricane

Non-fiction objective: To locate and note main points in a text.
Setting the homework: Explain that the text contains about 15 points, however, they are not all equally important. The task is to pick out four of the most important points.
Differentiation: More confident learners could be asked to rewrite their four main points into a paragraph of connected prose.
Back at school: Discuss the points chosen. Some flexibility should be allowed – what makes a 'main point' is sometimes a matter of interpretation. The first of the following points, plus any other three (though not 4 and 5, as they are similar points) would be a good answer:
1. A hurricane is a very strong wind.
2. Hurricanes are about 250 to 450km across.
3. The strength of hurricanes is measured on a scale of 1 to 5.
4. The strongest hurricane of the century was Hurricane Gilbert.
5. In Britain, the worst hurricane was in 1987.
6. Modern weather forecasts can give warning of hurricanes.
Link to *100 Literacy Framework Lessons Y3*: NFU1, Phase 1, Days 4 and 5: highlighting key points and note making.

Page 85 Notes

Non-fiction objective: To make notes.
Setting the homework: Ask the children to compare the example encyclopedia entry with the notes very carefully. They will see that the notes are brief, that abbreviations have been used and that only the main points have been included. They should remember this to make similar notes on the next encyclopedia entry.
Differentiation: This exercise can be extended for more confident learners, by giving them longer or more difficult extracts on the same subject.
Back at school: The note-making exercise could be extended as suggested above, or the skill could be applied to research for another subject.
Link to *100 Literacy Framework Lessons Y3*: NFU1, Phase 1, Day 5: note-making.

Page 86 TV report

Non-fiction objective: To watch and analyse broadcast information to identify presentational techniques and language.
Setting the homework: Ensure the children understand each of the headings in the grid, and perhaps spend a few minutes modelling how to complete it, using a brief film clip. Also discuss how to decide which are the key points; ask: *If you were telling someone about this, what are the first four things you would say?*
Back at school: Children can compare results in small groups, including new vocabulary they noted. A block chart could be made of the features ticked, to see which are the most and least common features noted.

Page 87 Crabs

Non-fiction objective: To locate and note main points in a text.
Setting the homework: This activity could follow on from page 84 'Hurricane'. Explain that there are about ten facts in this passage and it is impossible to include them all in a summary (or it would not be a summary). Children should therefore pick out the five facts that they think are the most important or interesting. Tell them to check that their five facts are spread through the whole passage (they should not just take the first five). The next step is to rewrite theses facts in a paragraph. Stress that this is more than just writing their facts one after another. The paragraph should be written in sentences. Sometimes it will sound better if two facts are placed in one sentence and linked by *and* or another conjunction (see page 111, 'Grace Darling'). Explain that the word *crab(s)* should not be used in every sentence. Using pronouns instead in some sentences will help the paragraph to sound like a connected whole.
Differentiation: Children who found page 84 difficult could be asked to omit the rewriting task.
Back at school: Share the summaries and discuss how well they meet the criteria explained above.

Page 88 Animals of the Arctic
Non-fiction objective: To write a non-chronological report.
Setting the homework: Tell the children that this activity will help them to learn how to arrange information in a report so that it makes sense for the reader. Tell them to use the openers to help them put the sentences in a sensible order, as well as reading the information within each sentence, looking for links that give clues.
Back at school: Display the sentences in a sensible order, and ask if anyone has a different order that they think works. Discuss how children made their decisions.

Page 89 Enjoyable, delightful, childlike – Core skills
Objective: To turn nouns and verbs into adjectives by adding suffixes.
Setting the homework: Revise the terms 'nouns', 'verbs', 'adjectives', 'suffixes'. Explain the activity is to match the root word with the appropriate suffix.
Differentiation: Very unconfident learners could be asked to do the first ten only.
Back at school: Review the correct words with suffixes.

Page 90 Shocking, dynamic, newsworthy! – Core skills
Objective: To turn nouns and verbs into adjectives by adding suffixes.
Setting the homework: Revise the terms 'nouns', 'verbs', 'adjectives', 'suffixes'. Explain that the activity is to match the root word with the appropriate suffix.
Differentiation: Very unconfident learners could be asked to do the first ten only.
Back at school: Review the correct words with suffixes.

Non-fiction – Unit 2 Instructions

Page 91 Instructions
Non-fiction objective: To analyse varied instructional texts.
Setting the homework: Ask the children to read each text and say what its purpose is. Emphasise that an important part of the homework is finding more examples in the categories of recipes, route-finders, timetables, plans, rules and instructions. Suggest some places for the children to look.
Back at school: Prepare a noticeboard or section of wall with headings for the six types of instructional text identified under 'Setting the homework' and ask the children to sort the instructions they have found and pin them up under the appropriate heading.

Page 92 How to make a book
Non-fiction objective: To analyse varied instructional texts.
Setting the homework: It may be a good idea to give out sheets of A4 blank paper as this will not be available in every home. Explain that, if a stapler is not available, the children should bring in the folded pages to be stapled in school. Finally, the children might be interested to know that this form of paper folding is used in the making of hardback books, and that, in the 18th and 19th centuries, readers had to cut the folds themselves.
Differentiation: More confident learners might like to experiment with making more of these foldings and stitching them together.
Back at school: Discuss the helpfulness of the instructions and examine the final products. It would be a good idea to use these miniature books for writing in.

Page 93 New mini-system
Non-fiction objective: To revise key organisational features of instruction texts.
Setting the homework: Explain that written instructions use a range of features to make them as clear and helpful as possible (such as: numbered or bulleted points and diagrams). Ask the children to find examples on the sheet. Encourage them to find real instructions and highlight them (with their helper's permission) in the same way.
Differentiation: Some of the language is difficult (though not essential to the task). Therefore, it would be useful to explain: *hazard, retro, amplifier, teak-effect, antenna, Dolby B* (a system which reduces hiss on tape), *trademark* and *licensing* to some children.
Back at school: Apply the same skill to instructions brought in by the children. Use these as a model for writing an instruction manual for a product. This will work best if a real purpose can be found, such as for a product made in a design and technology lesson.

Page 94 Hide and seek

Non-fiction objective: To analyse instructional texts; to revise key organisational features.

Setting the homework: Explain to the children that in order to write clear sets of instructions, they first need to know the way instructions can be organised, and the important things that need to be included. Tell them that they need to say why they have underlined a particular feature on the sheet, with a few words of explanation.

Differentiation: Less confident readers could just underline the features.

Back in school: Small groups of children can compare their work before each group's spokesperson feeds back their key points to the class.

Link to *100 Literacy Framework Lessons Y3*: NFU2, Phase 1: analysing texts and identifying key features.

Page 95 Giving directions

Non-fiction objective: To plan and orally rehearse instructional sequences.

Setting the homework: Give the children some spoken instructions to follow in class as a model, such as drawing a simple picture. Tell them they do not have to write every word they will say – just make brief notes using key words that they will use to tell somebody their directions.

Differentiation: You could suggest some children might like to draw the route before writing their notes.

Back at school: Children tell a partner their route, using their notes. Children could read out their route, for you to follow on a local street map on the board.

Link to *100 Literacy Framework Lessons Y3*: NFU2, Phase 2: planning oral instructions.

Page 96 What's wrong here?

Non-fiction objective: To analyse varied instructional texts, revising key organisational features and identifying language conventions.

Setting the homework: This would be a good follow-up to looking at the key features of instructional texts in class. Ask the children what important things should be included in a good set of instructions – language and organisational features.

Differentiation: A list of key features could be provided for less confident readers (see helper's notes); they should find where these could fit in the text.

Back at school: In groups, children compare their results, marking common elements on an A3 version of the sheet. Display each group's annotated sheets for all to compare.

Link to *100 Literacy Framework Lessons Y3*: NFU2, Phase 1: analysing texts and identifying key features.

Page 97 How to make a healthy sandwich

Non-fiction objective: To analyse varied instructional texts, revising key organisational features and identifying language conventions.

Setting the homework: This would be a good follow-up to looking at the key features of instructional texts. Ask the children what important things should be included in a good set of instructions – language as well as organisational features.

Differentiation: A list of key features could be provided for less confident readers (see helper's notes on page 96); they should find where these could fit in the text.

Back at school: In groups, children compare their results, marking common elements on an A3 version of the sheet. Display each group's annotated sheets for all to compare.

Link to *100 Literacy Framework Lessons Y3*: NFU2, Phase 1: analysing texts and identifying key features.

Page 98 How do you do it?

Non-fiction objective: To record a process and use this to draft instructional texts.
Setting the homework: The children will need to have had some experience of reading, analysing and writing instructions before doing this activity. Talk with them about the programmes they might watch, and reassure them that their instructions do not have to be very detailed, but should include language features of instructional texts.
Differentiation: Children likely to need a lot of support need only write a few words for each step.
Back at school: Children read their instructions to a partner, who tells the writer if they would be able to follow the instructions.
Link to *100 Literacy Framework Lessons Y3*: NFU2, Phase 1: watching an instructional programme.

Page 99 'SS' – Core skills

Objective: To explore the use of 's' and 'ss' in words.
Setting the homework: Explain the task. Warn children to take extra care with the last three words. They may use a dictionary if necessary.
Back at school: Go over the exercise, then monitor the use of this letter string in children's day-to-day writing.

Page 100 Possible... and probable! – Core skills

Objective: To recognise and spell the suffixes '-ible' and '-able'.
Setting the homework: Explain that the reason these endings are confused is that both the 'i' and the 'a' are pronounced as a light 'uh' sound in most words. This is a perfectly correct pronunciation as many unstressed vowels are said in the same way in English. The best way to learn the endings is to follow the tip on the bottom of the page.
Differentiation: Check that less confident learners understand all the words in the list.
Back at school: Give children a quick test on the endings and share any additional words that children thought of. Monitor these spellings in day-to-day writing.

Page 101 Looking for a misplaced exit? – Core skills

Objective: To learn to spell words starting with 'mis-', 'non-' and 'ex-'.
Setting the homework: Ensure the children know what a 'prefix' is. Tell them to use a dictionary to help with this activity, to be sure the spelling of their chosen words is correct.
Differentiation: Give less confident spellers a set of simpler words from which to choose, so that they do not select words that are too difficult for them. They could be asked to just choose one new word for each group.
Back at school: Pairs of children can test each other on their chosen words. See which were the most common choices.

Non-fiction – Unit 3 Information texts

Page 102 King Arthur

Non-fiction objective: To compare presentation of information in print and IT texts.
Setting the homework: Discuss the different ways in which information is available today, for example books, DVDs, CDs, the internet and so on. Explain that the homework sheet focuses on a web page and an information book page. Stress that the sheet only shows the beginning of each text. The children should draw on their own experience of using both books and the internet to compare the two different types of sources.
Back at school: Share ideas with the whole class and, if possible, set up an investigation using real websites and books.

Page 103 Seaside index

Non-fiction objective: To locate information.
Setting the homework: Explain that the children should use the homework sheet as a starting point, and then move on to a real reference book if a suitable one is available.
Differentiation: It might be a good idea to leave out the timing element for some children so that they do not feel under pressure.
Back at school: Apply the skill to a real research context.

Page 104 Be a librarian
Non-fiction objective: To use a library classification system.
Setting the homework: Briefly recap on the main points of the Dewey Decimal system. Then ask the children to imagine that they are librarians and a new batch of non-fiction books has just come in. The librarian's job is to classify them and put them on the shelves. Knowing the range of numbers is a great help in using a library.
Differentiation: The hard part for less confident learners is linking titles to categories, especially when the links are not obvious. Helpers can be asked specifically to support this.
Back at school: Visit the school library and investigate the Dewey Decimal system in use with real books. Apply the skills to a research task.

Page 105 My favourite things
Non-fiction objective: To decide how to present information and make informed choices by using structures from different text types.
Setting the homework: Ask children to talk to a partner about things they are interested in. Be prepared to make suggestions for children who have no special areas of interest. Tell them that the activity is just a plan – they don't have to find the actual information.
Back at school: Back with the same partners, children share their activity results. With the whole class, find out which were the most common sources of information, and presentation types. Children could carry on to find the information and complete their chosen presentation.

Page 106 Buy it now!
Non-fiction objective: To read and evaluate a wide range of simple persuasive texts.
Setting the homework: Display an advert on the board and annotate it to highlight the features listed on the sheet, to ensure the children understand what they are looking for. Reassure them that it doesn't matter if their chosen advert doesn't have all the features listed. Briefly explain the types of features they should include (see sheet).
Back at school: Ask how many children found examples of each type of feature listed, seeing if there were any that were less frequent than others. Children can compare their adverts with a partner.
Link to *100 Literacy Framework Lessons Y3*: NFU3, Phase 2: recognising the features of persuasive texts.

Page 107 TV adverts
Non-fiction objectives: To read and evaluate a wide range of simple persuasive texts.
Setting the homework: Ask the children to suggest the type of words they might be looking out for when they do the activity, and list them on the board. Tell them that it is a good idea to spread the task over several sessions, and to use different TV channels if possible, to get a wider range of examples.
Back at school: Groups of children compare their results, and a spokesperson feeds back to the class. Did they notice any differences according to time, channel, product or programme type?
Link to *100 Literacy Framework Lessons Y3*: NFU3, Phase 2: work on TV advertising.

Page 108 Wear your helmet!
Non-fiction objective: To begin to use words, pictures and other communication modes to persuade others when appropriate to particular writing purpose.
Setting the homework: Ask the children to list what they already know about the features of persuasive adverts. Remind them to think of the audience they are targeting with their poster, and that they should aim for a simple, clear design to get their message across quickly.
Differentiation: You could give less confident writers a list of possible words to use.
Back at school: Display the posters for the children to evaluate. Discuss the features they thought worked particularly well.
Link to *100 Literacy Framework Lessons Y3*: NFU3, Phase 3: work on persuasive language/road safety.

Page 109 Good idea, bad idea

Non-fiction objective: To begin to use words to persuade others when appropriate to particular writing purpose.

Setting the homework: Choose one or two other controversial statements to demonstrate the types of arguments that might be raised against them. Encourage the children to think of a good variety of responses.

Differentiation: Less confident writers can write one reason for each statement.

Back at school: Use the children's responses as the basis for a class debate on each of the topics. After each has been debated, take a vote to see whether the children's persuasive arguments were successful.

Page 110 Safely to school

Non-fiction objective: To begin to use words to persuade others when appropriate to particular writing purpose.

Setting the homework: Tell the children that as this is a formal letter, it is not the same as writing to a friend. Ask them for two or three reasons they might include. Tell them to group related material in paragraphs – maybe just two or three.

Differentiation: You could give some children lists of key words that they might include.

Back at school: Ask some children to read out their letters for the class to give positive comments about, linked to the objective.

Link to *100 Literacy Framework Lessons Y3*: NFU3, Phase 3: work on persuasive language/road safety.

Page 111 Grace Darling – Core skills

Objective: To use connectives to join sentences.

Setting the homework: Define the term 'connective', using the definition and examples on the sheet.

Differentiation: All children should be able to do the cloze exercise with more or less support, but some children may struggle with the terminology at this stage.

Back at school: Quickly go over the exercise, then ask the children to look at the first draft of a piece of their own writing. See if they can improve any of their sentences by joining two short sentences into one with a conjunction or by substituting a different conjunction where they have used *and*.

Page 112 Time sequence – Core skills

Objective: To explore time-sequence words.

Setting the homework: Explain that the task is based on the Battle of Hastings. The task is to choose appropriate time-sequence words and phrases to fill the gaps. All the words and phrases in the list should be used only once.

Differentiation: More confident learners should be particularly encouraged to find additional time-sequence words.

Back at school: Go over the exercise and share new time-sequence words that the children have found. The children should apply the skill by looking over old stories and recounts that they have written.

Page 113 Commotion and confusion – Core skills

Objective: To recognise and spell the suffixes '-tion' and '-sion'.

Setting the homework: Explain that the reason these endings are confused is that both are pronounced 'shun'. So, the only way to learn the words is by practising.

Differentiation: Check that less confident learners understand all the words in the list.

Back at school: Give children a quick test on the endings and share any additional words that children thought of. Monitor these spellings in day-to-day writing.

Poetry – Unit 1 Poems to perform

Page 114 Dialogue Between Two Large Village Women
Poetry objective: To rehearse and perform poems.
Setting the homework: Explain that part of the fun of performing this poem is to pronounce the words phonetically (that is, as they are spelled) and hear an echo of the West Indian accent.
Differentiation: More confident learners, and those who wish to, could improvise the scene that the women are talking about, or a new scene with these two characters.
Back at school: Ask for volunteers to perform the poem and any new scenes.
Link to *100 Literacy Framework Lessons Y3*: PU1, Phase 1: work on conversational poetry and performing poems.

Page 115 Why?
Poetry objective: To construct verses for a poem using a model.
Setting the homework: Explain that patterns of repetition are often used instead of rhyme, especially in modern poetry. Ask the children first to add a few extra verses to the poem (a verse in this case being a statement followed by *Why?*) and then to try a whole new Why? poem.
Back at school: Ask for volunteers to perform their poems in pairs.

Page 116 Overheard on a Saltmarsh
Poetry objective: To rehearse and perform poems.
Setting the homework: Poetry began thousands of years ago as an oral performance and this is still an important aspect of poetry. This poem by Harold Munro was written to be performed and the homework requires children to read the poem with their helper and plan a performance.
Back at school: Discuss ideas for performance of the poem, including simple movements, for example crouching to suggest a goblin. Discuss how the situation could be developed through improvisation. Give them five minutes to discuss ideas in pairs, then ask for volunteers to perform the poem and improvise a continuation.

Poetry – Unit 2 Shape poetry and calligrams

Page 117 Shape up!
Poetry objective: To compose shape poems and calligrams.
Setting the homework: Go over the definitions on the sheet, ensuring the children understand the difference between a calligram and a shape poem.
Back at school: Compile a class collection of calligrams and shape poems.
Link to *100 Literacy Framework Lessons Y3*: PU2, Phases 1 and 3: composing shape poems and calligrams.

Page 118 Shape poems
Poetry objective: To read and make comparisons between poems.
Setting the homework: The children should already have had some experience of looking at both types of poetry, so that this activity acts as reinforcement. Remind them that it is the shape of the subject that inspires shape poems, while the words themselves are used as the basis for calligrams.
Back at school: Ask the children to feed back the differences they noted and use these for a discussion. Take a vote for which type of poem the children prefer. Ask groups of children to read the poems out to the rest of the class.
Link to *100 Literacy Framework Lessons Y3*: PU2, Phase 1: reading and comparing poems.

Page 119 Comparing poems

Poetry objective: To make comparisons between poems.
Setting the homework: Choose two poems, songs or ballads by the same writer (or writers) to compare and give the children copies of these.
Differentiation: Less confident learners may have difficulty writing about verse form. They could be given a simpler version of the sheet with this section omitted. You could ask more confident learners to go into more detail when writing their short essay.
Back at school: Share the children's ideas about the two songs or poems.

Page 120 Spider spider

Poetry objective: To compose shape poems using language effects and making decisions about form.
Setting the homework: The children should have read several shape poems before doing this activity. Tell them that they can jot down words and phrases on the back of the sheet before they write their poem, and remind them that it does not have to rhyme.
Differentiation: Less confident writers could write simple adjective/noun phrases to describe aspects of spiders.
Back at school: Pairs of children can compare and read their poems. Choose examples from their work to write inside a large spider shape displayed on the wall.
Link to *100 Literacy Framework Lessons Y3*: PU2, Phase 3: writing shape poems.

Page 121 Abstract nouns – Core skills

Objective: To make abstract nouns by adding a suffix to a noun or adjective.
Setting the homework: Revise the term 'noun'. Discuss the names of things and then the names of some abstract ideas, such as *love*, so that the difference between concrete and abstract nouns can be explored.
Differentiation: Less confident learners may be able to say the abstract nouns but have trouble writing them. Helpers will be able to assist with this.
Back at school: Go over the abstract nouns in the second column while children mark their own.

Poetry – Unit 3 Language play

Page 122 Cats!

Poetry objective: To read, discuss and analyse a range of poems that play with language.
Setting the homework: Tell the children that the invented words describe what cats might do, or look like. Ask them to look out for capital letters to spot the names of breeds of cat.
Differentiation: Send a note to helpers of less confident readers, explaining that they should listen out for the invented words as the helper reads the poem.
Back at school: Discuss the words found and perform the poem together.

Page 123 Moths and Moonshine

Poetry objective: To read and analyse poems that play with language and to devise own poems.
Setting the homework: Define alliteration. Note that it is sounds that alliterate, not letters, so 'f' and 'ph' alliterate, hard 'c' and 'k', and so on. When the children write their poems, ask them to focus on alliteration only – they do not have to make them rhyme.
Differentiation: Less confident learners should be spared the more complex points of the definition (see above) and should use the simpler definition given on the homework sheet. Explain that a few lines of poetry or an alliterative slogan will be sufficient for the writing task.
Back at school: Share the children's alliterative poems. Investigate alliteration further by exploring its use in advertising and in early English poetry, for example in a good translation of Anglo-Saxon riddles.

Page 124 Playing with rhymes

Poetry objective: To build up a poem that follows a model seen in examples read earlier.

Setting the homework: Recite some well-known nursery rhymes together. Choose one to create new versions of, such as 'Ladybird, Ladybird, Fly Away Home', or 'Twinkle Twinkle Little Star', modelling how the children should work on the activity, and asking them for ideas. How many different versions can you write?

Back at school: Ask children to read out their new versions to a partner, then ask for some to be read to the class. Each child could word process or handwrite their favourite to be included in a class anthology or display.

Link to *100 Literacy Framework Lessons Y3*: PU3, Phase 2: writing new versions of nursery rhymes.

Page 125 Create-a-poem

Poetry objective: To play poetry games and use these as the basis for creating their own nonsense poem.

Setting the homework: Read some nonsense poetry to the class, such as that of Edward Lear, and point out the nonsense words that he created. Show the children how to complete the grid on the homework sheet, using different word parts.

Differentiation: Starting lines could be provided for less confident writers.

Back at school: Groups of children share their poems, reading them aloud. Choose some to be read out to the class. Make a book or display of the poems.

Page 126 Word play

Poetry objective: To analyse poems that play with language.

Setting the homework: Explain that the sheet contains four funny poems in which the poets have played with words to create the humour. Read one aloud before the children go home.

Differentiation: All the children will enjoy the humour of these poems, although not all will be able to articulate how the humour is achieved.

Back at school: As the homework involves reading and discussing, with no written outcome required, it is important to follow it up in the classroom. Ask the children to share their responses and select a few to read the poems aloud.

Page 127 A gaggle of geese – Core skills

Objective: To understand and identify collective nouns.

Setting the homework: Revise the terms 'noun' and 'collective noun'. The children should note that collective nouns are singular, even though they refer to a group of things. Go through the example on the sheet.

Differentiation: Delete the harder examples for less confident learners. Encourage more confident learners to invent their own.

Back at school: Go over the correct pairings and share any new collective nouns that the children have invented.

NARRATIVE

Name   Date

On the beach

■ Read the passage and talk to your helper about the pictures you see in your head as you read each part of the description. What senses have been used to describe the setting? You might want to underline the parts you think are most important in setting the scene.

The beach was deserted except for a woman walking her dog some way in the distance. The tide was out, leaving a wide stretch of wet sand that glistened in the early morning sunlight. Here and there were shallow rock pools with barnacle-covered boulders that might have had crabs hiding beneath them if you looked carefully, and slippery seaweed that could catch you unawares if you didn't watch where you put your feet. Seagulls screamed overhead, or bobbed on the waves while black and white oystercatchers with long orange bills poked deep into the sand for food.

Even though it was a bright morning, there was a strong wind, whipping up white-topped waves and blowing dried seaweed across the sand. With the wind came the familiar smell of the beach, a mixture of salt, sea and freshness while above, a few wispy clouds moved quickly across a blue sky. A perfect day to be on the beach!

Illustrations © Theresa Tibbetts/Beehive Illustration

Dear helper
Objective: To identify different things that can be included in the description of a setting.
Task: Read the passage with your child, then look at it again more closely, talking about the images it suggests. Help your child to notice where the senses have been used to give as full a description as possible, for example: *Which words are about sounds? Which parts are the most important? Why?*

PHOTOCOPIABLE 📖SCHOLASTIC
www.scholastic.co.uk

Name	Date

Story settings

■ Read these story settings. Underline or highlight the words and phrases that describe each scene.

That summer, we went to Jamaica. The first thing I noticed when I stepped off the plane was the heat – a clinging, steamy heat like a Turkish bath. Then there was the tangled tropical jungle. It was like going back into the Jurassic age. By the time we reached our hotel it was dusk, and the air was full of the music of cicadas and tree frogs.

The street was a very ordinary street, a street of rows. There were rows of houses in dull red brick – all the same. There were rows of cars, one on each side of the straight stretch of tarmac. A row of shops at the top end offered some variety. The biggest shop, the Supersave supermarket, had huge glass windows with posters shouting about the latest bargains. There had once been a bank next to it, but that was now boarded up and the boards were covered with graffiti.

My name is Sarah and I am the first human being to see this scene with my own eyes: Mount Olympus on Mars. It is a volcano, but is much bigger than any mountain on Earth. As I gaze up to its jagged, red peak, I feel that I could climb up it all the way back to Earth. Let me tell you how I got to be in this awesome place.

The tunnel was low, and it was very hot. Tanis crept along on all fours with great care. He was afraid that he would spring one of the traps left by the dead Pharaoh to protect his tomb. Suddenly he came to a great chamber. He stood up, raised his lamp, and was amazed at the brilliantly coloured pictures on the walls.

Illustrations © Theresa Tibbetts/Beehive Illustration.

Dear helper
Objective: To compare a range of story settings and select words and phrases that describe scenes.
Task: Read these story settings with your child and discuss what brings them to life.

NARRATIVE

Name   Date

Picture the setting

◧ Choose one of these picture settings and write a detailed description of it. Use your imagination to add to what you can see.

Outer space

Enchanted castle

Deserted house

School

Illustrations © Theresa Tibbetts/Beehive Illustration.

Dear helper
Objective: To write a description of a story setting using a picture stimulus.
Task: Talk about each picture with your child and help them choose the one they find most interesting.

PHOTOCOPIABLE ▨ SCHOLASTIC
www.scholastic.co.uk

Name   Date

What's most important?

■ Use this diagram to plan the setting for a story. Choose words that describe the mood and atmosphere of the setting. Put two or three words in each zone, with the most important ones in the middle.

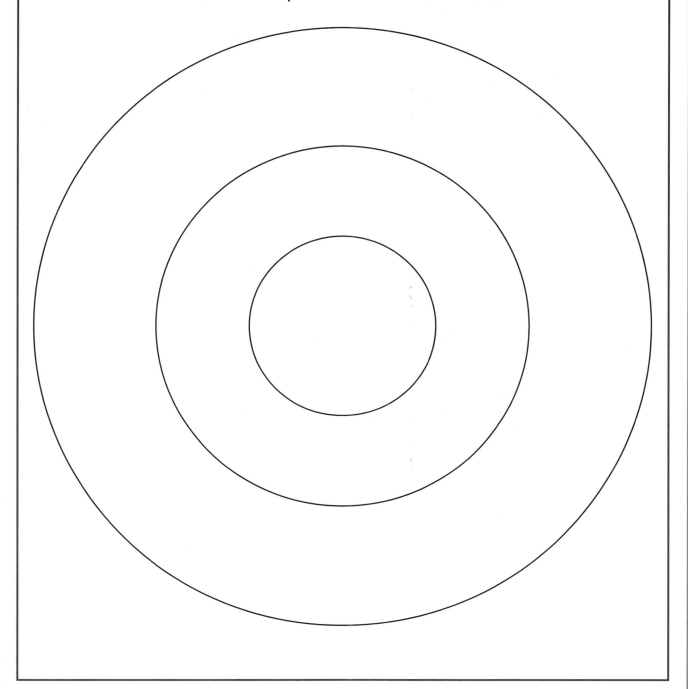

Dear helper
Objective: To choose key words to describe a setting.
Task: Your child will have been given a theme for planning this setting. Talk with them about what might be included, and help them to choose words they could use to describe the setting. Together, decide on their levels of importance. Your child should write the words in the appropriate places on the diagram.

NARRATIVE

NARRATIVE

Name

Date

In the kitchen

- Imagine you are in the kitchen below. Use your senses to write in the boxes the things you would see, hear, taste, touch and smell.

See	Hear	Taste	Touch	Smell

Dear helper
Objective: To use the senses when describing a setting.
Task: Talk about the picture with your child, imagining you were in the kitchen, and help them to fill the boxes.

Illustrations © Theresa Tibbetts/Beehive Illustration

PHOTOCOPIABLE **SCHOLASTIC**
www.scholastic.co.uk

Name   Date

Settings on screen

■ Watch one of your favourite TV programmes that has different settings – a cartoon is a good example. While you are watching, write in the boxes below about some of the things that have been used to create atmosphere and mood in the settings. An example has been given to help you.

Music	Camera angles	Lighting	Close-ups and long shots
Loud and fast when there's a storm	Looking down from a high window	Dark in the forest, flashing eyes	Close-up of dog looking sad

Dear helper
Objective: To analyse and describe settings from a visual stimulus.
Task: Your child has been learning about how filmmakers use different techniques to create atmosphere and mood. This will help them to create interesting settings in their own work. Talk about what might be a good programme to choose. Writing while watching is hard to do, so watch the programme with them, helping them to spot the things they are looking for.

NARRATIVE

Name   Date

Creating an atmosphere

■ It is important to choose the right language to create the atmosphere we want in our writing. For the two settings below, choose words, phrases or sentences that you might use to describe the atmosphere in each place.

■ You should try to make them sound like very different places. There is an example to help you.

A large dense forest	A small country wood
It was as black as night.	Sunlight filtered through the leaves.

Dear helper
Objective: To choose vocabulary that creates an atmosphere for a particular setting.
Task: Talk with your child about what it might be like in each of the settings. *What might you see or hear? How might you feel?* Each pair of descriptions should almost be opposites of each other, so that different atmospheres are created.

How commas help

■ Highlight or underline all the commas in the following text, then read it aloud.

■ Talk about how commas make reading easier.

After their father is arrested, 13-year-old Elinor is trying to hold the family together. Here, she is trying to cheer them up on a cold April day.

The weather turned colder. On 1 April, like a bad joke, there was a fall of hailstones, rattling against the windows and knocking over the daffodils. Then in the night it snowed, a wet, sloppy snow, already dripping down from the trees when they woke, and greying to slush on the pavements. Bambi had a bad cold.

"I hate this country," Sophia muttered.

"It'll be better soon," Elinor told her. "It'll be lovely next week, you'll see."

"Next week may be too late."

"Bambi's only got a cold. He won't die of it. He's getting better already. Wait till the sun comes out– "

"If it ever does," Sophia said gloomily.

"Wait and see," Elinor said, forcing herself to sound cheerful.

from A Kind of Thief *by Vivien Alcock*

Text © 1991, Vivien Alcock; illustrations © Theresa Tibbetts/Beehive Illustration.

Dear helper

Objective: To note where commas occur in reading and discuss how they help the reader.

Task: Listen to your child read this text, or share the reading. Talk about how commas help to make reading easier.

Name   Date

Punctuation pointers

◗ **Punctuation** makes texts easier to read. Explore this in two steps in the following passages.

Step 1: No punctuation

◗ Read this passage aloud.

the problem was mondays every monday mum took katie to the saddle club but because it was seven miles away she didn't think it was worth coming home so she waited that meant kimberley had to wait too and kimberley hated horses she liked harleys much better harleys are american motorbikes with high handlebars and low seats kimberley thought it would be much more fun to ride a harley than a horse

◗ Say if reading it was easy or difficult and explain why.

◗ Rewrite the passage adding capital letters and full stops. Use the back of this sheet.

Step 2: Dialogue not punctuated or set out clearly

◗ Read this passage with someone else. One person should read Katie's lines and the other, Kimberley's lines.

I don't know what you see in horses. They're stupid! said Kimberley. They're better than Harleys anyway, replied Katie. You can't go a hundred miles an hour on a horse! You can't jump on a Harley! There are no brakes on a horse, they're dangerous! They're safer than Harleys! Well, horses go lame! So what. Harleys go rusty and fall to pieces and get sent to the scrap yard!

◗ Say if reading it was easy or difficult and explain why.

◗ Write the above passage with speech marks.

◗ Start a new line for each change of speaker. Use the back of this sheet.

Illustrations © Phil Garner.

Dear helper
Objective: To understand the need for punctuation.
Task: As children develop an appreciation of punctuation, their ability to use it effectively is increased. Listen while your child reads the passage in Step 1 and share in the reading of the passage in Step 2. Help with punctuating both passages. Encourage re-reading of the passages to check that all punctuation has been included.

Name	Date

Theseus and the Minotaur

■ Read this description of Theseus meeting the Minotaur in the labyrinth.

Theseus looked over his shoulder towards the entrance of the labyrinth which was now just a small pinprick of light in the distance. Gradually, his eyes adjusted to the darkness, as he felt his way cautiously through the damp tunnel. Theseus knew that somewhere in this gloomy place the Minotaur was waiting, and he felt his heart pounding, as his ears strained for sounds of the terrible monster. He knew that a great battle lay ahead of him; a battle he was determined to win. Theseus was brave – but was he a match for the Minotaur?

Suddenly, Theseus froze. From around a corner to his right came deep, rasping breaths and the scraping of heavy hooves on the stony floor. He flattened his body against the slimy tunnel walls, and felt for his sword. And then – there it was – the Minotaur! Towering above him, the great beast strode steadily forward, its red eyes glinting through the darkness.
A strange mixture of man and bull, the monster's gigantic head had curving horns and wild hair but its arms and hands were those of a human. It stood tall on its powerful legs, with hooves that would be dangerous weapons if you got too close. Even its tail could lash a mighty blow. Steam snorted from the creature's nostrils before it let out the loudest bellow Theseus had ever heard, an awful sound that echoed around the labyrinth.

■ On the back of the sheet, draw a picture of the Minotaur. In the space around your picture, write some of the things that Theseus might have thought as he went through the labyrinth, and when he first saw the Minotaur.

Illustrations © Theresa Tibbetts/ Beehive Illustration.

Dear helper
Objective: To engage with a written text and identify a character's feelings.
Task: This story is part of a famous Greek myth. Read the passage with your child and talk about what the Minotaur looked like. Talk about how Theseus might have felt as he went into the labyrinth, knowing he was getting closer to the monster, and what his thoughts might have been when he actually saw it. Encourage your child to think of different things that Theseus might have felt and thought.

Name   Date

NARRATIVE

Typical story language

■ Here are some typical examples of story language found in folk and fairy tales. Think of some more examples (or find them in books) and write them on the back of this sheet.

■ Try to write your own story in the same style.

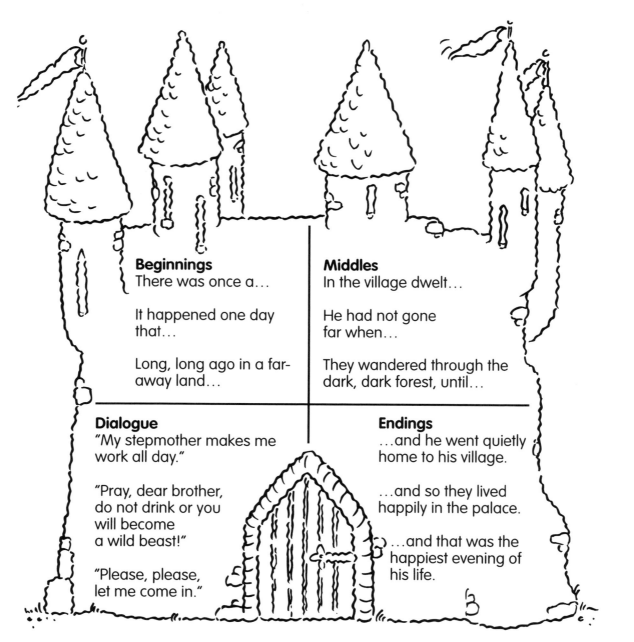

Beginnings
There was once a…

It happened one day that…

Long, long ago in a far-away land…

Middles
In the village dwelt…

He had not gone far when…

They wandered through the dark, dark forest, until…

Dialogue
"My stepmother makes me work all day."

"Pray, dear brother, do not drink or you will become a wild beast!"

"Please, please, let me come in."

Endings
…and he went quietly home to his village.

…and so they lived happily in the palace.

…and that was the happiest evening of his life.

Illustrations © Theresa Tibbetts/Beehive Illustration.

Dear helper
Objective: To explore the styles and voices of traditional story language.
Task: Read through the examples with your child. Ask: *Do you recognise them from any particular story?* Help your child think of – or find – other similar examples. Talk about how some of these phrases could be used in a story.

Name	Date

The choosing

■ Read this story, then answer the questions.

There was once a young shepherd who wished to marry. He knew three sisters who were all equally pretty, so it was difficult for him to choose between them.

So he asked his mother for advice. She said, "Invite all three to our house and put some cheese on the table before them. Then watch how they eat it."

Next day, the young man invited the three sisters to his house and put a plate of cheese in front of each one. The first girl swallowed the cheese with the rind on. The second girl hastily cut the rind off the cheese, but she cut it so quickly that she left much good cheese with it, and threw that away as well. The third girl, however, peeled the rind off carefully, and wasted none of the cheese.

The young man asked his mother what she thought of the three girls. She replied, "Take the third for your wife."

This he did, and lived contentedly and happily with her.

The Brothers Grimm

1. Why did the shepherd find it difficult to choose between the sisters?

_____

_____

2. What did the way they ate the cheese show about them?

_____

_____

3. How do you think he should have found the most suitable girl?

_____

_____

4. What kind of a wife do you think the third girl will be?

_____

_____

Dear helper
Objective: To identify typical story themes.
Task: Share the reading of the story with your child, then discuss the theme by exploring situations where you or your child have had to make choices. Ask: *What helped you to decide?* Finally, discuss the questions in preparation for your child's written answers.

NARRATIVE

Name	Date

Quest myth plan

■ Cut out the cards and arrange them in different ways to create a framework for different quest stories. Use one card from each category.

■ Tell the stories to your helper.

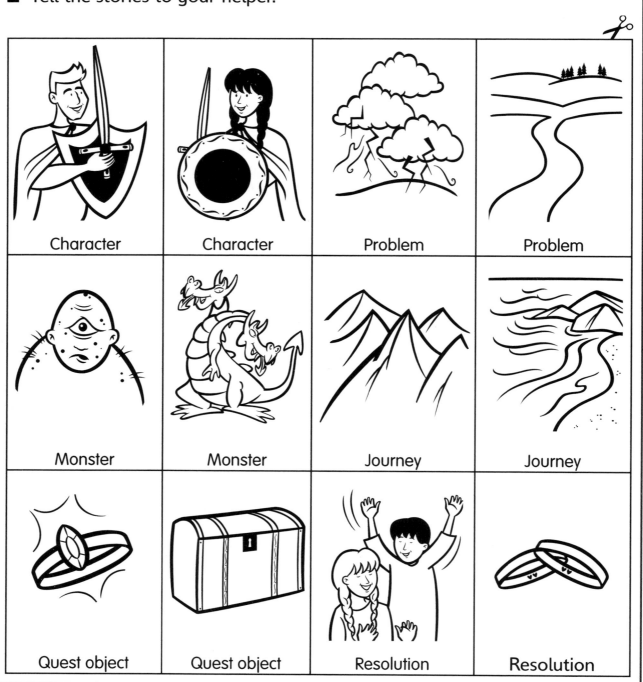

Character	Character	Problem	Problem
Monster	Monster	Journey	Journey
Quest object	Quest object	Resolution	Resolution

Illustrations © Theresa Tibbetts/Beehive Illustration.

Dear helper
Objective: To use oral storytelling to plan a quest myth.
Task: Help your child to sequence the cards, choosing different combinations to create different stories. You may decide to give your character more than one problem to solve, or use both journey cards to make the quest more difficult. Help your child tell the story if they get stuck.

PHOTOCOPIABLE ■SCHOLASTIC
www.scholastic.co.uk

Name	Date

Plot cards

■ The cards below give six basic plots for a story. Talk about each of them, then choose one to develop into a story plan. (If you wish, adapt the ideas freely and use ideas from other cards.)

Dragon

A terrible dragon is destroying the countryside and eating maidens.

The king promises half his kingdom to anyone who can kill the dragon.

Many knights try to kill the dragon and fail. Describe what happens to one of them.

A poor boy/girl decides to have a go.

Three trials

A young man asks for a princess' hand in marriage, but her father says he must first pass three trials.

He undergoes three strange trials, with three clever ways to solve them. The princess could help him secretly.

Princess in disguise

There is a terrible monster that everybody is frightened of.

A knight is hired to kill the monster. He fights the monster, but just before he kills it, the monster asks for a kiss. Is it a trick? Should the knight agree or should he kill the monster?

He kisses the monster and it turns into a beautiful princess.

Quest

Far away over the mountains is a fabulous treasure.

The hero/heroine has many adventures on the journey.

What do they find when they get there? Is it what they expected?

Fortune seeker

A family is so poor the mother cannot afford to feed her children. She sends them out to seek their fortune.

Tell the story of each one.

The first two fail and the third succeeds.

Three wishes

The hero/heroine does a good deed one day, for example rescues a drowning cat.

In return, they are given three wishes. Tell the story of each wish.

Do the wishes work out well or badly?

Illustrations © Theresa Tibbetts/Beehive Illustration.

Dear helper

Objective: To plan main points as a structure for story writing.

Task: Discuss these six plots with your child. During discussion, encourage them to elaborate by adding other ideas. Finally, your child should choose one of the plots and write their ideas as a detailed story plan. Encourage them to use ideas from other cards if they wish to.

Name	Date

Story game

◾ Turn a story into a board game. Write some of the main problems in squares with instructions such as: **Miss a turn** or **Go back two spaces**.

◾ Write some of the good things in the story in some squares with instructions like: **Take an extra turn** or **Move ahead one space**. Make counters for the main characters.

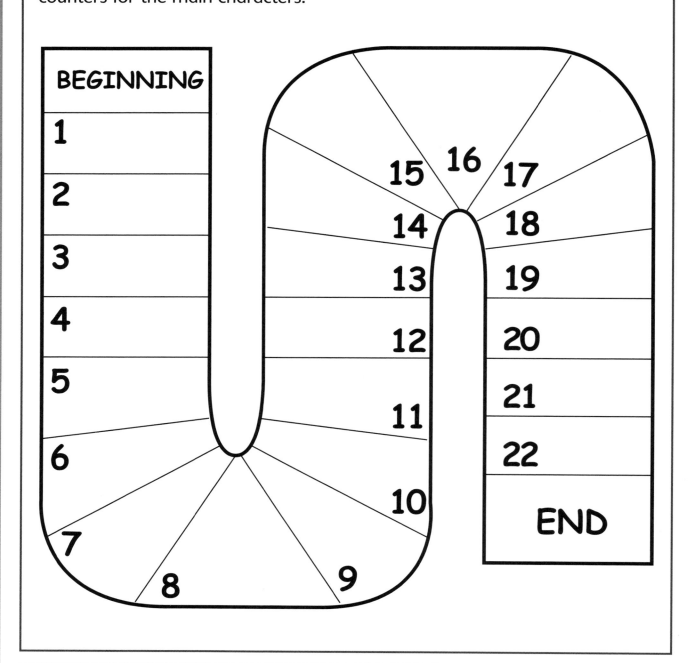

Dear helper

Objective: To describe and sequence key incidents in a variety of ways.
Task: Your child will also bring home a story with this sheet. Help them to pick out key incidents from the story and place them on the blank game board. Play the finished game with your child.

Name	Date

How the elephant got a long trunk

◾ Read this well-known myth.

"Keep away from that lake, Ellie," said her mother. Now, Ellie the Elephant had not thought about the lake before, but suddenly it sounded interesting. When her mother wasn't looking, she decided to take a peek.

She found the lake and was disappointed. It was just like a large puddle after all. But all that walking had made her thirsty, so she decided to have a drink – she didn't know that Alligator was looking for food! Ellie dipped her short trunk into the water (in those days, all elephants had short trunks). Alligator thought that it was a fish, so he swam up and bit Ellie's trunk.

"Let go of my trunk! Let go of my trunk!" she shouted. But Alligator didn't hear and started pulling Ellie's trunk even harder. They both tugged and tugged and Ellie's trunk stretched and s-t-r-e-t-c-h-e-d!

After a while, Alligator gave up – this fish was too tough – and he went after a smaller fish that had just swum by.

Ellie's trunk was very sore – and very long. She felt silly at first, but soon found out how useful it was. She could pick things up with it, give herself a shower with it, and many more wonderful things. Of course, when Ellie grew up and had babies, they all had long trunks too – and this is how elephants got long trunks!

Illustrations © Theresa Tibbetts/Beehive Illustration.

◾ Plan a similar myth of your own. Here are some ideas:

- ❑ How the mouse got a long tail
- ❑ How the chameleon learned to change colour
- ❑ How the crocodile learned to swim
- ❑ How the parrot learned to talk
- ❑ How the snake lost its legs
- ❑ How the rabbit got big ears

Dear helper
Objective: To write a story plan for a myth using a theme from one read.
Task: Remind your child that a myth is a story that tries to explain something we don't understand or how something came to be. Share the reading of the myth with your child, then discuss ideas for writing a new myth of the same kind.

NARRATIVE

Name	Date

The sequel game

Robin Hood	Pandora's Box	The Ugly Duckling
King Arthur	The Hare and the Tortoise	Goldilocks and the Three Bears
Jack and the Beanstalk	Aladdin	The Three Billy Goats Gruff

◾ Cut out the story cards, mix them up and lay them face down.

◾ Take it in turns with a partner to pick up a card and tell a sequel to the traditional story – a follow-on story that uses some of the same characters and settings. Do this several times.

◾ Then choose the idea you like best and make notes for a written story sequel.

Illustrations © Theresa Tibbetts/Beehive Illustration.

Dear helper
Objective: To plan a sequel to a well-known traditional story.
Task: Ensure your child is familiar with all the stories on the cards. If there are some that are unknown, discard these and only use the familiar ones. Encourage your child to base their sequel on some of the characters and settings from the original story, but to think about different plots.

Name	Date

A pair of trousers

! **Remember: Singular** means one of a thing. **Plural** means more than one.

■ Sort these words into singular and plural. Write each one under the correct heading in the grid below.

trees	children	CDs	hippopotami	cars	shoes	bus
flies	calves	potatoes	a pair of trousers	sheep	fish	trousers
	giraffe	flock	cassette	dog	roof	zoo

Singular	Plural

Illustrations © Theresa Tibbetts/Beehive Illustration.

Dear helper
Objective: To understand the terms 'singular' and 'plural' and to identify words appropriately.
Task: Most of the words are easy to sort, but some will require extra thought. Discuss the more difficult words with your child.

Name   Date

Multi-purpose prefixes

■ These prefixes are often used to invent new words:

Prefix	Meaning
anti-	against
cyber-	to do with the internet
Euro-	to do with Europe
hyper-	very big
mega-	very big
micro-	very small
mini-	small
multi-	many
super-	very good or large
web-	to do with the internet

■ Look at these examples of new words, and then make up some of your own.

Prefix	Meaning
megaproblem	very big problem
minihomework	a small homework
webschool	a school on the internet

Illustrations © Theresa Tibbetts/Beehive Illustration.

Dear helper
Objective: To make up new words using prefixes.
Task: Remind your child that a 'prefix' is a word-part added to the beginning of a word to change its meaning. Go over the prefixes and their meanings, then help your child to think of new words using the prefixes.

Name   Date

Multi-purpose suffixes

■ These suffixes are often used to invent new words:

Suffix	Meaning	Example
-able	able to be	kissable
-agram	comes delivered to your door	gorillagram
-athon	long, hard work	marathon
-cred	a good reputation in	street-cred
-friendly	liking or acting favourably towards	girl-friendly
-hostile	disliking or acting unfavourably towards	school-hostile
-ise/ize	makes a noun into a verb	hospitalise
-less	without something	brainless
-phobia	fear of	arachnophobia
-speak	a way of speaking	edu-speak

■ Look at these examples of new words, and then make up some of your own.

New word	Meaning
homeworkathon	lots and lots of homework
schoolphobia	fear of school
teacherise	make a person into a teacher

Illustrations © Theresa Tibbetts/Beehive Illustration.

Dear helper
Objective: To use knowledge of suffixes to generate new words.
Task: Remind your child that a 'suffix' is a word-part added to the end of a word to change its meaning. Go over the suffixes and their meanings, then help your child to think of new words using them.

NARRATIVE

Name   Date

Will-o'-the-wykes and bogles

Doctor Grant's lights were still on. His curtains were the colour of ripe peaches. And a lantern, swaying in his porch, threw a pool of soft, shifting light over the flagstones and gravel outside the front door.

Annie stared and stared as if she had never seen bright light before. In the gloom of the great storm, nothing had looked quite definite and many things looked frightening: the reaching arms of the tree, the fallen body of the milk churn, the gleam and flash of water. There was the danger, too, of meeting these chancy things that only come out at night – will-o'-the-wykes and bogles and boggarts and the black dog, Shuck... and worst of all there was the ghost.

■ Read this passage from *Storm* by Kevin Crossley-Holland. How would you describe the atmosphere that is created?

_____

_____

_____

■ Highlight the language that helps to build up the atmosphere.

Dear helper
Objective: To investigate language that is used to create atmosphere in a story.
Task: Help your child to find the right words to describe the atmosphere in the extract and to highlight or underline the words and phrases that help to create it. Discuss what might happen next.

PHOTOCOPIABLE ▪SCHOLASTIC
www.scholastic.co.uk

Text © 1985, Kevin Crossley-Holland; illustrations © Theresa Tibbetts/Beehive Illustration.

Name

Date

Pirates

■ Read these descriptions of fictional pirates. Highlight the adjectives in each description. Highlight any words or phrases that show the characters' feelings and their relationships with others.

Long John Silver

(the pirate in *Treasure Island* by Robert Louis Stevenson)
I was sure he must be Long John. His left leg was cut off close by the hip, and under the left shoulder he carried a crutch, which he managed with great skill, hopping about upon it like a bird. He was very tall and strong, with a face as big as a ham – plain and pale, but intelligent and smiling. Indeed, he seemed in the most cheerful mood, whistling as he moved about among the tables, with a merry word or a slap on the shoulder for his favourite guests.

Captain Hook

(the pirate in *Peter Pan* by James M Barrie)
He was carried in on a chair by his men – whom he treated like dogs. His face was corpse-like, and his hair was dressed in long curls, which looked like black candles and gave him a threatening look. His eyes were of the blue of the forget-me-not, and very sad, except when he was plunging his hook into you, when two red spots appeared in them and lit them up horribly. In dress he copied the style of King Charles II and in his mouth he had a holder of his own design which enabled him to smoke two cigars at once. But undoubtedly the grimmest part of him was his iron claw.

Dear helper
Objective: To discuss characters' feelings, behaviour and relationships.
Task: Read and discuss these descriptions of fictional pirates Long John Silver and Captain Hook. Help your child to highlight the descriptive words and phrases asked for. Discuss what these extracts show about the characters.

Name   Date

Emil

■ Read this character description of Emil. Then answer the questions below.

Perhaps you will have already heard of Emil, who lived at Katthult in Lönneberga in Småland. You haven't? Well, well! But I can assure you there isn't a single person in Lönneberga who hasn't heard of that naughty little boy. He got into more kinds of mischief than there were days in the year, and frightened the people of the district so much that they wanted to send him far away from Sweden. They did, really! They collected a lot of money and took it to his mother and said, 'Maybe there's enough there to pay for sending Emil to America.'

They thought Lönneberga would be far more peaceful without Emil, and of course that was true, but Emil's mother was very angry indeed and flung the money all over the place.

'Emil's a dear little boy,' she said, 'and we love him just as he is.'

And Lina, the maidservant in Katthult, said, 'Besides, we ought to consider the Americans, too. They've never done us any harm; so why should we plague them with Emil?'

from Emil Gets Into Mischief *by Astrid Lindgren*

1. Emil's actions aren't described, so how do we know how naughty he is?

_____

2. What does Emil's mother think of him? Why do you think her feelings are different to everyone else's?

_____

3. How do you think Emil felt when he heard about the townsfolk's plans to send him away?

_____

Text © 1979, Astrid Lindgren; Illustrations © Theresa Tibbetts/Beehive Illustration.

Dear helper
Objective: To explore and discuss a main character.
Task: Read through this description with your child and talk about what it is that brings the character to life. Discuss answers to the questions, sharing your ideas as well. Ask: *Would you like to know more about Emil? Why or why not?*

Name   Date

Character card

■ Write a reference card about a character in a book that you have been reading. Sketch a portrait in the picture frame.

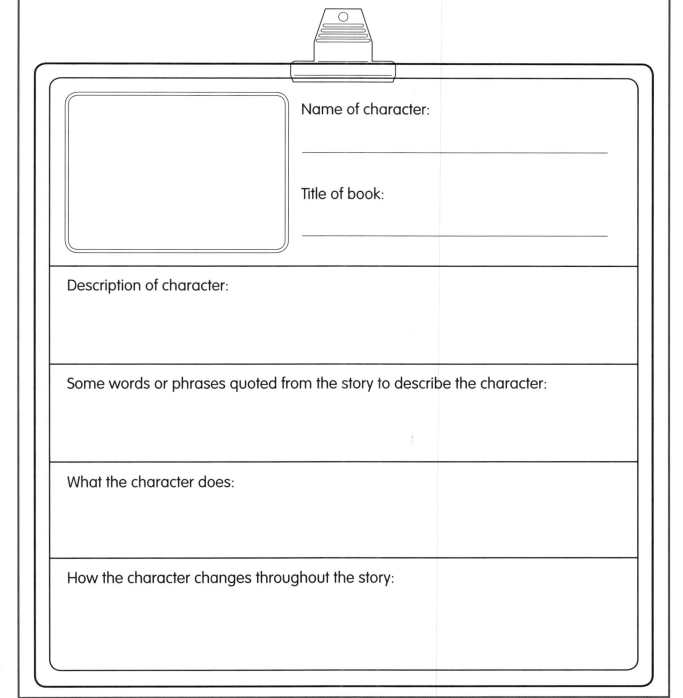

Name of character:

_____

Title of book:

_____

Description of character:

Some words or phrases quoted from the story to describe the character:

What the character does:

How the character changes throughout the story:

Dear helper
Objective: To write about a character from a story.
Task: Your child will have brought home a story or notes for use with this activity. You can help by discussing each aspect of the character card with your child and looking for suitable evidence in the story.

Name	Date

Layla's adventure

◾ Read this passage from an adventure story.

Layla looked behind her one more time before she opened the door to the cellar. She could hear the sound of the wind roaring down the chimneys of the old house, and the rain lashing against the huge windows, but luckily nothing else. Carefully she descended the stone steps, with only the feeble beam of her torch to pick out the way. Quickly she scanned the jumble of junk piled up in the cellar. Layla knew what she was looking for, but would it still be there? Or would Magnus have got there before her? No! There it was, just where she had been told, behind a group of old barrels; the unmistakeable outline of a model sailing ship. But no ordinary model – for Layla knew that this one held a special cargo beneath its decks.

◾ Imagine you are Layla, writing to a friend to tell them about your adventure. Write your letter on the back of this sheet, telling your friend how you felt and what you were thinking as you went into the cellar.

Illustrations © Theresa Tibbetts/Beehive Illustration.

Dear helper
Objective: To retell an incident from a story in the form of a letter.
Task: Read the passage with your child, picking out the different things that Layla saw and heard, and what she might have been thinking. Remind them that they will write the letter in the first person; using the word 'I'. It will be all right to use some of the words from the original, but information about thoughts and feelings will make the letter more personal.

PHOTOCOPIABLE 📖 **SCHOLASTIC**
www.scholastic.co.uk

Name	Date

Once upon a time

◗ Read these story openings and talk about what kind of story they might lead into.

◗ Add some more story openings in the blank boxes.

A long time ago, something so strange happened that you'll never believe it.
Deep in his dreams, Samir heard his sister's voice and began to wake himself up.
The house was empty. The door was nailed up and the empty window frames banged in the wind. It was spooky.
Sally lived with Auntie May and her two cats. She was a shy little girl who liked to sit quietly and read books.
Once upon a time, there was a poor widow who had three sons. "I have nothing to give you," she said to them. "You must go and seek your fortune elsewhere."
"Aaah – it's an alien!" screamed Joanne.

Dear helper
Objective: To investigate sentences for story openings.
Task: Discuss these story openings with your child. Talk about what kinds of stories they might lead into. Help your child to find – or make up – more openings.

NARRATIVE

| Name | Date |

Happily ever after

■ Read these story endings and talk about what kind of story might have led up to them.

■ Add some more story endings in the blank boxes.

I hope you enjoyed my story – but I told you that you'd never believe it!
Samir woke up at last. "It was just a dream after all! I thought I woke up, but that was all part of the dream!"
The house was beautiful again. It had a new roof and windows, and the lawn was neatly mowed. It wasn't spooky anymore.
"That was quite an adventure for a shy person like me," thought Sally as she settled down to read a book.
The prince knocked on the door of the little cottage and an old woman answered it. "Don't you recognise me?" asked the prince. "I am your son!"
"It all goes to show," said Darren, "how the imagination can play tricks when it's dark!"

Illustrations © Theresa Tibbetts/Beehive Illustration.

Dear helper
Objective: To investigate sentences for story endings.
Task: Discuss these story endings with your child. Talk about what kinds of stories might have led up to them. Help your child to find – or make up – more endings.

PHOTOCOPIABLE ■SCHOLASTIC
www.scholastic.co.uk

Name   Date

Cliffhangers

■ For each of the cliffhangers below, write one or two sentences that might start the next part of the story.

Mihika carefully pushed the library door closed and tiptoed away, afraid she might be heard.

I didn't know which way to turn. Straight ahead and I would be sure to fall into the crevasse, but the blizzard was so strong I couldn't see clearly in any direction. What was I to do?

The great meteor storm continued around the fragile craft as it hurtled, bombarded by giant rocks, deeper into space.

Dear helper
Objective: To develop an adventure story from a cliffhanger ending.
Task: Talk with your child about how TV programmes often use 'cliffhangers' at the end of an episode, so that we want to watch next time. Help them to think up possible ways in which each of the stories above might continue.

NARRATIVE

Name	Date

Improve a story

■ On a separate piece of paper, rewrite this draft story by adding more detail. Use the notes to help you.

■ Plan more adventures for Pegleg the pirate.

First draft of story	Notes to improve it
Pegleg the pirate got his name from his wooden leg. His ship was disguised as a merchant ship, but on deck he had 20 cannons hidden under packing cases.	Describe Pegleg in more detail – make him frightening! Describe his ship in more detail – what was it called, how many masts, sails and so on?
His crew were the fiercest pack of thieves afloat.	Give an example of their fierceness – for example describe a quarrel between them.
One day the lookout saw a sail on the horizon. "Sail!" he shouted.	
"Give chase!" said Pegleg.	Use synonyms of **said** for more dramatic effect.
They soon caught up with the ship, which was a heavily-laden merchant ship on its way to the American colonies.	Describe the merchant ship in more detail.
"Surrender!" said Pegleg.	
"Never!" said the captain of the ship.	Describe the captain in more detail – as a contrast to Pegleg, make him pleasant and kind.
He thought he could fight off the pirate because he had four cannons and his men had pistols and cutlasses. A terrible battle followed which the merchant captain lost.	Describe the battle in much more detail – this is the most exciting point in the story. Say what happened to the brave captain.
After the battle, Pegleg decided that he would find an island and treat his men to a feast as a reward for capturing the merchant ship.	

Dear helper
Objective: To write a longer story.
Task: Read through the draft story and notes with your child and discuss ways of extending the story by adding more detail. Help your child to plan more adventures for Pegleg.

PHOTOCOPIABLE ▪SCHOLASTIC
www.scholastic.co.uk

Puppy problem

■ Use this paragraph plan to help you to write a story in paragraphs on a separate piece of paper.

Sam was a new puppy who had just come to live in Lucy's house.
(Describe Sam. What did he look like? What games did he like to play?)

Sam liked living in Lucy's house, but he kept getting into trouble.
(Describe some of the things he does wrong – for example, chewing cushions, getting mud on the carpet, or weeing in the house.)

Then one day, Lucy said, "You will have to go to school to be trained!"
(Describe how Sam is trained at dog school.)

When he had finished at school, Sam knew how to behave.
(Describe how Sam behaves after the training.)

After that, Sam managed to keep out of trouble – well, most of the time!

Illustrations © Theresa Tibbetts/Beehive Illustration.

Dear helper
Objective: To use paragraphs in story writing.
Task: Share ideas with your child about what might be written in each paragraph. When your child is writing the story, check that the rules of paragraphing are being followed correctly.

Name _____   Date _____

Combine sentences

■ Combine these sentences by writing the appropriate **connectives** on the line. Look for more than one possible connective.

Connectives: although, and, as, because, but, for, until, when, where, while

1. The girls were frightened _____ they heard the thunder.

2. They got soaked _____ it rained unexpectedly.

3. They decided to take shelter _____ the rain stopped.

4. Tara felt uneasy _____ they entered the old house.

5. Zara tried to switch on the lights _____ there was no electricity.

6. Tara opened a cupboard _____ she found a skeleton.

7. She was about to scream _____ Zara pointed out that it was plastic.

8. The girls tried to sleep _____ they were too nervous.

9. Zara woke up early _____ a cock crowed loudly.

10. Tara was happy _____ the rain had stopped.

Extension

■ Use the sentences to write a story. Make them more interesting by combining them and adding more detail. You can use the back of the sheet or a separate piece of paper.

Dear helper
Objective: To construct sentences by combining two shorter sentences.
Task: Read these sentences with your child, taking a column each and trying out different conjunctions orally. Your child will then find it easy to write in appropriate conjunctions.

Name   Date

Non-stick

◾ The prefixes **non-**, **ex-**, **co-** and **anti-** are often used to make up new words. Here are some examples of recent words:

non- (means not)	**ex-** (means former)	**co-** (means joint)	**anti-** (means against)
non-fiction non-metal non-stick	ex-girlfriend ex-husband ex-policeman	coeducation costar coworker	antibiotic antidote antifreeze

◾ Make up your own new words. Some starter ideas can be found below. Note that, although **metal** only works with one prefix, some words will work with more than one.

Words to try	Word + prefix	Meaning
metal	non-metal	not a metal
alien		
chocolate		
computer		
nuclear		
person		
reading		
school		
tangle		
teacher		
vegetable		

◾ Think of some of your own words to add prefixes to. List them on the back of this sheet.

Dear helper
Objective: To recognise and spell the prefixes 'non-', 'ex-', 'co-' and 'anti-'.
Task: Remind your child that a 'prefix' is a word-part added to the beginning of a word to change its meaning. Check that your child does not add prefixes in a thoughtless way. They must be able to say what the new words mean.

NARRATIVE

Name   Date

Book review

■ Use this writing frame to help you write a book review for other children in your class. Make notes here, then write out the review in full on a separate sheet.

This is a review of   by
The book is about
The main character is The author describes the character as "
The book is set in   This is vividly described by the author in these words: "
The part of the book that I most enjoyed was   However, I did not like
My overall opinion of the book is

Dear helper
Objective: To write a book review for a specified audience.
Task: Your child will have brought home a book to review (or notes on a book). Help your child to think about what to put in each paragraph and then to build up the prompts into continuous prose.

Name	Date

Author hunt

■ See how much you can find out about an author of your choice. You can find information on the internet, on book covers, at the library, by asking people or from books written about them.

■ What can you put under the headings below?

Author's name_____

Background information about the author

Titles of some of the books

Illustrators of the author's books

Type of books (for example humour, adventure)

Which books you like and why

Illustrations © Theresa Tibbetts/Beehive Illustration.

Dear helper
Objective: To research a particular author and explain reading preferences.
Task: Help your child to select a favourite author, and to source information about them. They will need supervision and probably some help if using an internet search engine. If you don't have the internet at home, your local library will probably have it available.

NARRATIVE

Name   Date

Dick King-Smith

▪ Plan and prepare the following text to be presented as a page on a website. Think about the following points:

- ❑ Which fonts will you use for headings and the main text?
- ❑ How will you arrange the different bits of text on the page?
- ❑ Will you include any pictures?
- ❑ Will you use columns or text boxes?

About Dick King-Smith

Dick King-Smith was born in Bitton, Gloucestershire on 27th March, 1922. He worked as a farmer for 20 years before becoming first a teacher and then, at the age of 55, a writer of stories for children. His first book was called *The Fox Busters*. He has now written more than 100 books, which have been translated into many languages and are sold all over the world. Most of his books are about animals, with the most famous probably being *The Sheep-Pig* which many people now know as *Babe*, as the book was made into a successful film.

He first writes his stories in longhand before typing them up on an old typewriter, and reading them to his wife to get her opinion. He and his wife first met when he was 13 and they now have three children and 12 grandchildren. He will not fly in an aeroplane and doesn't like nuts, turnips or pineapples, but loves the English countryside, his German Shepherd dog and writing books for children.

Some well-known books by Dick King-Smith

The Sheep-Pig	A Mouse called Wolf	George Speaks
The Hodgeheg	Emily's Legs	Daggie Dogfoot
Sophie's Snail	The Queen's Nose	

Dear helper
Objective: To prepare a page of text to be redesigned as web page.
Task: If you can, look at some web pages as a basis for how the information above could be rewritten in a more visual format. Talk about how the information might be divided into sections, and help your child to mark on the sheet how they plan to do this, annotating where they would make changes or add things like pictures. They can then make a rough plan of how their page will look, on the back of the sheet.

Name	Date

Letters

■ Here are some guidelines about paragraphs you should remember when you are writing letters:

▢ Start a new paragraph for each new topic.

▢ **Handwritten** letters usually indicate a new paragraph by indenting the first line (by about 1cm). There are not whole blank lines between paragraphs.

▢ **Printed** letters often use block paragraphs. Block paragraphs show a new paragraph by leaving a whole blank line. There are no indentations.

■ Organise this letter into paragraphs. Write it out on a separate piece of paper or the back of this sheet.

Dear Tom,

We are settling in well in our new house. I miss our old house, but I really like my new bedroom. It is much bigger than the old one, so there's plenty of space for my toy soldiers. My sister has been moaning because she says that my bedroom is bigger than hers. This is true, but she's got the best view. By the way, did I leave this month's 'Wargame' magazine at your house? I've looked for it everywhere and I can't find it. I want it because there's a great Zargian battle tank that I want to buy which was in the advertisements. The best news of all is that my dad says that you can come and stay in the summer holidays. We'll have a great time! Bring all your toy soldiers and we'll have a battle. I bet I'll win, 'cause I'll have my new battle tank by then!

See you soon,
Tim

Extension

■ Write a short letter to a friend in paragraphs.

Illustrations © Theresa Tibbetts/Beehive Illustration.

Dear helper
Objective: To organise a letter into simple paragraphs.
Task: Read the guidelines with your child, ensuring they understand them. Then check to see if they apply them correctly in rewriting the letter. If appropriate, encourage them to write a letter to a friend.

NARRATIVE

Name _____   Date _____

Letter to an author

■ Use this writing frame to help you write a letter to an author.

(Your address)_____

_____

_____

(Date)_____

Dear_____,

My name is _____ and I am a pupil

at _____. I am

writing to say how much I enjoy your books.

My favourite book is _____. I liked it because

_____

_____

The one big question I would like to ask you about your writing is

_____

_____

I am looking forward to reading more of your books, and perhaps meeting you if you should visit our school.

Yours sincerely,

_____

Illustrations © Theresa Tibbetts/Beehive Illustration.

Dear helper
Objective: To write a letter to an author about a book.
Task: Help your child to draft a letter to an author using the writing frame. In particular, discuss appropriate questions to ask the author.

Name

Date

Letter to a character

■ From a book you have been reading, choose one of the main characters, and write a letter to them. Imagine you know them quite well. You can write about other characters in the story and some of the things that happened, telling them what you thought or how you felt, and asking them questions.

Name of the book _____

Author _____

Character _____

Dear _____   _____

_____

_____

_____

_____

_____

_____

_____

_____

Illustrations © Theresa Tibbetts/Beehive Illustration.

Dear helper
Objective: To plan and write a letter to a book character.
Task: Help your child to decide on the book and character. It should be one they know well enough to write an interesting letter. Encourage them to think of questions they would ask the character if they were able to speak to them. Help them to structure the letter into two or three paragraphs, each with a slightly different focus.

Prefix game

Prefixes

un	de	dis	re
un	de	dis	re
un	de	dis	re
un	de	dis	re
un	de	dis	re

Roots

well	frost	please	build
happy	code	agree	fill
tidy	form	honest	visit
lucky	fuse	appear	play
do	mist	obey	write

How to play

1. Cut out and shuffle the cards.
2. Deal the cards to each player. The players should separate their cards into roots and prefixes.
3. Player 1 puts down any card – a prefix or a root.
4. Player 2 must then try to finish the word by using a prefix or a root from their cards. They win a point for making a word, and an extra point for defining it!
5. Player 2 then puts down a new card and it is the next player's turn to finish the word.
6. If a player cannot finish the word, the next player can try to do so.
7. The winner is the player with the most points once all the cards have been put down.

Illustrations © Theresa Tibbetts/Beehive Illustration.

Dear helper
Objective: To recognise and spell common prefixes and how these affect meanings.
Task: Play this game with your child. It may help to colour the root and prefix cards different colours. Remind your child that a 'prefix' is a word-part added to the beginning of a word to change its meaning. For each word made ask: *How has adding the prefix changed the meaning of the word?*

Name _____   Date _____

Where's my partner?

Some words tell you the **gender** of the person or animal they describe. They tell you if it is male or female. The suffix **-ess** indicates that the word is feminine.

◼ Match the masculine and feminine forms of the following words. The first one has been done for you.

Masculine	Feminine
actor	lioness
author	baroness
baron	authoress
duke	hostess
enchanter	instructress
god	manageress
heir	poetess
host	actress
instructor	mistress
lion	princess
manager	shepherdess
master	sorceress
murderer	tigress
poet	waitress
priest	duchess
prince	priestess
shepherd	enchantress
sorcerer	goddess
tiger	heiress
waiter	murderess

◼ In these days of equal opportunity, some feminine words are rarely used. Highlight these words in the above list.

Illustrations © Garry Davies.

Dear helper
Objective: To explore gender suffixes.
Task: The matching task is easy. However, your child may need help to identify those feminine forms that are rarely used today.

NARRATIVE

Name   Date

Finger puppets

■ On the shapes below draw faces and features of the characters in a story you know well. Cut them out and make them into simple cylinder-shaped finger puppets.

■ With your helper, act out a scene with the characters. You decide what they say, and how they say it.

Dear helper
Objective: To act a simple scene from a story, using puppets as characters.
Task: Have a conversation about stories your child knows well, and choose four key characters from the story you choose. Let your child enjoy drawing and colouring the puppets and take turns to be the voices for the puppets acting a scene from the story.

NARRATIVE

| Name | Date |

How should I say that?

■ When you write a playscript, you need to give the actors stage directions, so they know how you want them to say the words you have given them. These are often adverbs.

■ Find the best words from the list to use as stage directions in the playscript below. Write them in the brackets.

| humbly | puzzled | excitedly | grumpily | explaining |
| cheerfully | impatiently | confused | warning | thinking |

Scene: *Aladdin in the cave. He has just picked up a lamp.*

Aladdin (_____): Huh. What's this? A rusty old lamp. I might as well clean it up a bit. (He rubs the lamp and a genie appears.)

Genie (_____): Greetings, oh Master!

Aladdin (_____): Master? What do you mean?

Genie (_____): I am your slave, oh Master! You rubbed the lamp to call me. I must do whatever you wish.

Aladdin (_____): Oh…oh…er…um…

Genie (_____): Well, make your mind up! What about your three wishes?

Aladdin (_____): Three wishes? What do you mean?

Genie (_____): He who owns the lamp has three wishes. I have the power to grant those wishes.

Aladdin (_____): Wow! That's fantastic! Right then, I wish…

Genie (_____): Take care, Master. Think carefully before you wish, or you may regret it.

Dear helper
Objective: To give stage directions for dialogue.
Task: Help your child to read the playscript, and talk about how each line might be spoken. Then choose a suitable word from the box to use as the stage direction. Some words may fit more than one place, but try to use each word just once. Finally, read the script, taking turns to be the characters, following the stage directions.

NARRATIVE

Name	Date

Play language

■ Plays use special vocabulary to describe features of how they are written. Can you match the vocabulary with its definition? Join pairs with lines. (You could use different colours for each pair).

stage direction	Names of all the characters in the play
dialogue	The setting for one part of the play
scene	When a character speaks directly to the audience
cast list	The words actors have to learn
script	When actors have a conversation in a play
props	What we call a play written down
aside	Objects actors use when they act the play
lines	This tells the actors how to speak and how to move

Dear helper
Objective: To learn technical vocabulary associated with plays.
Task: Ask your child which of these they already know, before helping them to work out those which may be less familiar.

Name	Date

Schoolbot

📕 Read this scene from a play and think about how you would prepare it for performance.

Scene 1: A classroom in the year 2020. The children are coming into the classroom, among them is a robot called Schoolbot.

Teacher:	Good morning, children. (*To Schoolbot*) Who are you?
Schoolbot:	(*in a metallic voice*) My name is Schoolbot.
Teacher:	(*looking around*) Where is David?
Schoolbot:	David sent me in his place.
Teacher:	Why did he do that?
Schoolbot:	Because he says that school is boring.
Teacher:	We aren't in the entertainment business, you know.
Schoolbot:	(*looking around*) So I see.
Teacher:	If David doesn't come to school, he won't learn anything and he won't be able to get a job.
Schoolbot:	I will get a job for him.
Teacher:	I'll have to see the headmistress about this later. (*To the class*) Get out your maths books and do numbers 1–100 starting on page 32. (*Aside*) That should keep them quiet for an hour.

A few moments later.

Schoolbot:	I have finished.
Teacher:	What? Already?
Schoolbot:	My Turbo 1000 brain can perform a million calculations per second.
Teacher:	(*sighing*) Now there's quick mental maths for you!

Extension

📕 On a separate piece of paper, write extra scenes for the play. Think about, for example, what Schoolbot is like at other subjects such as PE and ICT. What happens at lunchtime? What might happen when David gets bored at home?

Illustrations © Theresa Tibbetts/Beehive Illustration.

Dear helper
Objective: To read, prepare and present playscripts.
Task: Read the script and help your child to prepare it for performance. Discuss ideas for extra scenes.

NARRATIVE

Name   Date

All in good time

- Read this playscript and prepare it for performance.
- Write an extra scene about what happens next week.

Mrs Scratchit:	This week, we are going to be studying a masterpiece of classic literature.
Billy:	Oh no!
Mrs Scratchit:	It's called *The Time Machine* by H.G. Wells. And to help us understand what it is about, my brother has made this working model of a time machine from the description in the book. *(Billy looks interested)*
Kirsty and Karen:	Oh no!
Mrs Scratchit:	Pay attention! Now, this lever here is used to go back into the past. *(She pulls the lever.)*
Billy:	*(Running to the window)* Hey, look, that tree is shrinking!
Karen:	*(Looking towards the road)* Where are all the cars?
Kirsty:	Why are there knights in armour on the school field?
Billy:	*(Realising what has happened)* It actually works!
Kirsty and Karen:	What works?
Billy:	That model time machine!
Karen:	Miss, it works! It works!
Kirsty:	Can we go to Ancient Egypt?
Karen:	Can we see the dinosaurs?
Mrs Scratchit:	How dare you interrupt my lesson! I thought I told you – this week we are studying classic literature.
Billy:	But what about the time machine?
Mrs Scratchit:	*(Unimpressed)* All in good time. If you work hard on the novel, I may consider taking you to Ancient Egypt next week.

Illustrations © Garry Davies.

Dear helper
Objective: To prepare, read and perform a playscript.
Task: Read the playscript with your child and discuss how it could be prepared for performance. Discuss ideas for writing an extra scene.

Name	Date

Scripting Cinderella

■ In the passage below, highlight or underline the words you would use if you were rewriting this as a playscript. Use one colour for the lines the actors would say and another colour for words that would be useful for stage directions.

Cinderella

Cinderella sat sadly by the fire, wishing that she had been able to go to the ball. Suddenly there was a flash of light and a puff of smoke.

"Oh!" gasped Cinderella, "Whatever was that?"

"Don't worry my dear," a voice spoke gently, "It is only me."

"But…who are you?" asked Cinderella, puzzled.

"I am your Fairy Godmother," the voice replied kindly, as out of the smoke walked a smiling, rather elderly lady carrying a magic wand and with a shining cloak around her shoulders.

Cinderella stood up. "I didn't know I had a Fairy Godmother," she said, sounding a little confused. "I'm not even sure I know what you are."

"Well, I will tell you, my dear," the Fairy Godmother said softly. "It is my job to take special care of you, and whenever you are feeling sad, or in trouble, I will do my very best to make it all better."

Cinderella was beginning to get excited. "If you really are a fairy," she said, "then you must be able to perform magic!"

"I certainly can," replied the old lady, smiling.

"Then…" Cinderella hesitated.

"Yes, my dear," interrupted the Fairy Godmother, "I can help you go to the ball at the palace."

"Oh! Fairy Godmother!" cried Cinderella. "That would be wonderful!"

"Yes, but remember this – you must leave before midnight when all my magic will stop," the old lady warned.

Illustrations © Theresa Tibbetts/Beehive Illustration.

Dear helper

Objective: To learn how to adapt a story into a play.

Task: Help your child to read the story, taking particular note of words and phrases that tell you how the dialogue should be spoken. Then ask your child to decide which parts of the story would be used as dialogue in a play version, and which words would be used as stage directions.

NARRATIVE

Name _____   Date _____

Planning a playscript

◼ When you plan a scene to be acted, you need to think of several things before you start to write. Use the questions below to help you plan the script you will be writing in school.

What will the title of your play be? _____

Where will the first scene be set? _____

Who are the characters, and what are they like?

_____

_____

_____

_____

How will the scene start? _____

_____

What will happen next? _____

_____

How will the scene end? _____

_____

What key words will you use as stage directions, and who might they be for?

_____

_____

Dear helper
Objective: To plan the outline for a short play.
Task: Talk with your child about each of the questions, helping them to decide on the answers. They should aim to have three or four characters in their scene, who should have different characteristics to make the scene more interesting.

Name	Date

Bored boy

■ Read this passage from *Schoolbot*, then turn it into a playscript using the example below as a starting point.

Bored with school, David sent a robot called Schoolbot in his place. The problem is, now he is bored with staying at home!

David, dozing in front of the TV, was woken up by Schoolbot coming home from school. "Good afternoon, David," said Schoolbot in his metallic voice.

"What's good about it?" said David grumpily.

"I thought you liked watching TV?" said Schoolbot.

"It's all repeats," said David, flicking through the channels with the remote control. "I bet you had more fun at school!"

"Well, we had an interesting lesson on the addition of fractions…" began Schoolbot.

"Yuk!" David interrupted.

"…and a great game of football in which I scored 27 goals!"

David sighed. "I haven't played football for ages," he said sadly.

"Oh, and Karen asked me for a date."

David sat up suddenly. He was surprised to find that he felt jealous. "And what did you say?"

"I said that I didn't have any dates, but I was sure she could get them from the local supermarket."

Playscript starter

Schoolbot:	(*in a metallic voice*) Good afternoon, David.
David:	(*grumpily*) What's good about it?
Schoolbot:	I thought you liked watching TV?
David:	(*flicking through the channels*) It's all repeats. I bet you had more fun at school!

Extension

■ On the back of this sheet, finish the playscript for the scene.

Illustrations © Theresa Tibbetts/Beehive Illustration.

Dear helper
Objective: To write a simple playscript based on a story.
Task: Help your child to compare the story version with the sample of playscript, and then to complete the playscript, following the style.

Mash

| asked | cried | declared | exclaimed | explained |
| pleaded | replied | said | shouted | snapped |

■ Choose from the synonyms of **said** above to fill the gaps in the story. You do not have to use all the words, and you can use any word more than once.

Schoolbot is a robot who has taken the place of one of the children at St Mark's Primary School.

At last the bell rang for lunch.

"Hey, Schoolbot!" _____ Tom. "Come and sit at our lunch table!"

"I am very sorry," _____ Schoolbot, "but I do not eat."

"Not eat?" _____ Tom.

"No," _____ Schoolbot. "I recharge my battery instead."

"Will you come and sit with us anyway?" _____ Tom.

Schoolbot went with Tom into the dining room and they sat down. Unfortunately, St Mark's Primary School has some very strict dinner ladies.

"Now, what's this?" _____ Mrs MacDuff to Schoolbot. "Why are you not eating?"

"Because it would give me a short circuit," _____ Schoolbot.

"No excuses!" _____ Mrs MacDuff, and spooned mashed potato into Schoolbot's mouth. There was a bang and a flash and Schoolbot fell to the floor.

Illustrations © Theresa Tibbetts/Beehive Illustration.

Dear helper
Objective: To choose alternative words to *said* to make dialogue more interesting.
Task: Remind your child that a 'synonym' is a word of similar meaning to another. Read this passage with your child and experiment with different synonyms of 'said' in the gaps. Then let your child make the final decision about which synonyms to write in.

Name	Date

Hot Sleepysaurus

■ Highlight all the speech marks in this story and then read it aloud.

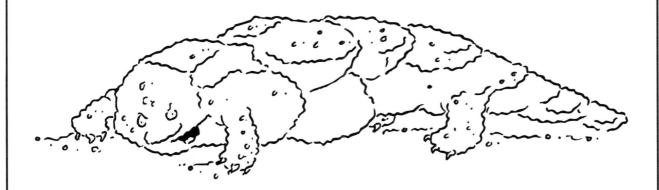

The Sleepysaurus is a creature like a rock garden that turns up at Bell Street Flats.
This is what happened when it began to get too hot:

The Sleepysaurus lay there in the sun getting hotter and hotter, and we all thought a lot.

"We can't carry baths," said Niki.

"And the Mean Man has taken away the hose pipe," said Rashid.

"What about buckets?" I said.

We got our buckets, and then we looked at the Sleepysaurus.

"How many bucketfuls do we need?" I asked Rashid and Niki.

"Hundreds!" said Rashid.

"Thousands!" said Niki.

"Millions!" I said.

"Billions!" said Rashid.

"Trillions!" said Niki.

"Hundreds of thousands of millions of billions of trillions!" I said. "And there's only one tap in the yard!"

from Our Sleepysaurus *by Martin Waddell*

Dear helper
Objective: To identify speech marks in reading.
Task: When your child has highlighted all the speech marks, take it in turns to read the dialogue and the narrated text (that is, the text not in speech marks).

Name   Date

Capital letters in speech

When you are writing speech, always use a capital letter after the first speech marks:

"**S**top!" said Miss Marvel.

When a line of speech is divided into two parts, the second part begins with a capital letter *only* if the first part ends with a full stop:

"Stop!" said Miss Marvel. "**T**hat's all wrong!"

But:

"Wait," said Miss Marvel, "**u**ntil all the children are here."

■ Add capital letters to the dialogue below. Don't forget the names and places!

"tomorrow we are going on a school trip to london," Miss Marvel announced.

"miss marvel, if I get travel sick," asked Karen, "what shall I do?"

"don't worry, karen, we'll take a bucket," said miss marvel.

"i get sick as well," said 15 other children.

"oh dear!" said the teacher. "that's rather a lot of you!"

"never mind," said tom, "we'll take a bathtub instead!"

Illustrations © Theresa Tibbetts/Beehive Illustration.

Dear helper
Objective: To use capital letters to mark the start of direct speech.
Task: Discuss with your child the use of capital letters to begin names, places and sentences. Then go over the explanation of this additional use of capital letters.

Name   Date

Willa's baby

◗ Highlight all the speech marks and other dialogue punctuation in this passage.

This passage, from Storm *by Kevin Crossley-Holland, describes the night that Willa's baby is born.*

"A cup of tea first," said Annie's mother, looking pleased and shiny.

"You said Christmas," protested Annie.

"You never can tell," said her mother. "Anyhow, early or late, storm or no storm, it's on its way. There's no stopping it now!"

"You could call it Storm," said Mr Carter unexpectedly.

"That's not a name," said Annie.

"Storm?" said Willa.

"Storm," repeated Annie's mother. "That's an old name in these parts."

"Shall I ring the hospital?" said Willa. "I know there's time but…"

"I'll ring while you get yourself packed and ready," said her mother.

"Ask them to come for me in half-an-hour," said Willa and, taking her tea with her, she went back upstairs to get ready.

Extension

◗ Write a piece of dialogue between two people, using speech marks and other dialogue punctuation correctly.

Name   Date

Fiction and non-fiction

■ Cut out these book cover cards and sort them into fiction and non-fiction.

■ Put the fiction into alphabetical order by author surname and non-fiction in alphabetical order by title. Paste the book covers down on a new sheet.

NON-FICTION

The Enchanted Frog	Dinosaurs	A Guide to Grammar	The Mystery of the Missing Munchies
Judy Gilbert	Andrew Simmons	Gillian Hunter	Arthur Snowden
The Adventures of Chuckling Charlie	The Story of Queen Victoria	Mr Stan, the Bicycle Man	Roman Britain
Susan Mathews	Mary Dennis	Joyce Leonard	Charlotte Gibbons
Pesky Peter and Other Stories	Operation Titanic	Computers and How They Work	The Dragon Who Lost His Fire
Pamela Hughes	Stephen Porter	A. S. Tagore	Alison McFee
Fun with Maths	The "I Can't Cook" Cookbook	Fluffy's First Birthday	Discover Hong Kong
Ashim Mehta	Sarah Cook	Michael Burns	Travel Guides Ltd

Illustrations © Theresa Tibbetts/Beehive Illustration.

Dear helper

Objective: To understand the distinction between fiction and non-fiction.

Task: Help your child to sort these books into fiction and non-fiction. Most are easy, but there are a couple that could be either. Discuss the categories in which these should be placed.

Name   Date

Fact or fiction?

■ Below are the opening lines from eight books. After each one write whether it is **fact** or **fiction**. If you are not sure, write **unsure**.

Elizabeth I was the daughter of Henry VIII. She was born in 1533 and became queen of England in 1558. She died in 1603.

_____

There was once a dog who had no home. His name was Sam. He was a mongrel, one of his ears was bitten off and he had a stumpy tail — which was probably why nobody wanted him.

_____

This is the story of a ship called the *Titanic*, which sank below the freezing waves of the Atlantic in 1912.

_____

Atlantis is a continent that used to be in the middle of the Atlantic Ocean. It was destroyed by an earthquake and sank below the waves thousands of years ago.

_____

"Hey! Give me my pen back!" shouted Savi when he saw that Tim was using it. "Be quiet!" ordered Miss Crotchet. "I want these notes finished by lunchtime!"

_____

An escalator is a moving staircase. The first escalator was set up in Paris in 1900. Escalators normally move at a speed of 2mph.

_____

Once upon a time, when dinosaurs roamed the Earth, a small lizard broke through its shell and entered the prehistoric world.

_____

Fushun (pronounced foo-shun) is a coal-mining area in a remote part of China.

_____

Dear helper
Objective: To understand the difference between fact and fiction.
Task: Many of the book beginnings are easy to classify as fact or fiction, but your child will need to discuss some of them. For example, the last one sounds like a fact, but does Fushun really exist? How could you check it?

Name   Date

Crocodiles

■ Compare these fiction and non-fiction passages and answer the questions below.

African Adventure

"Help!" shouted the boy.

He had been crossing the river when a crocodile had caught him by the foot. I ran to him and grabbed his arms and pulled as hard as I could. The boy screamed with pain. The crocodile glared at me with his tiny evil eyes. He thrashed his long grey tail to increase his pull, and I felt my grip slacken…

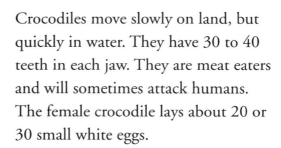

FICTION

Crocodiles

Crocodiles are reptiles. They are found in Africa, Asia, Australia and Central America. The largest is the Indian salt-water crocodile which can grow up to 7 metres in length.

NON-FICTION

Crocodiles move slowly on land, but quickly in water. They have 30 to 40 teeth in each jaw. They are meat eaters and will sometimes attack humans. The female crocodile lays about 20 or 30 small white eggs.

Illustrations © Theresa Tibbetts/Beehive Illustration.

■ Which passage, fiction or non-fiction, gives the most realistic description of the crocodile?

■ Which passage is the most exciting to read? Why?

■ What are the differences in the way the two passages are set out?

Dear helper
Objective: To notice differences in the style and structure of fiction and non-fiction.
Task: Read these two passages with your child and discuss the questions.

Name	Date

Arctic challenge

◼ Use the contents page below and write which chapter you would look at to find the following information.

Information	Chapter name	Information	Chapter name
Bowhead whales		Arctic terns	
Melting ice caps		Background information on the Arctic	
Narwahls		Arctic foxes	
Day length at different times of year		Polar bears	
Robert Peary's voyage to Greenland		Animal visitors to the Arctic	

Contents

Chapter	Page
The Arctic Circle – an introduction	4
Land mammals of the Arctic	7
Birds of the Arctic	11
Sea creatures of the Arctic	14
Arctic migration	17
Seasons in the Arctic	20
Arctic night and day	23
Arctic expeditions	25

Illustrations © Theresa Tibbetts/Beehive Illustration.

Dear helper
Objective: To use a contents page to find information.
Task: Read through the sheet with your child and help them to decide which chapter they would find the information in. Start with the ones they find easiest – they do not have to be done in any particular order.

NON-FICTION

Name   Date

NON-FICTION

Hurricane

- Read this information about hurricanes and underline four key points.
- Write them in the space below.

A **hurricane** is a very strong wind, that blows in a circle around a centre of low pressure. The centre of a hurricane is known as the 'eye'. Hurricanes are about 250 to 450km across. The strength of hurricanes is measured on a force scale of 1 to 5. Hurricanes of force 1 (the mildest) have winds of at least 120kph. Hurricanes of force 5 have winds of over 250kph. The strongest hurricane of the 20th century was Hurricane Gilbert. It hit Jamaica and Mexico in 1988 with winds up to 350kph. In Britain, the worst hurricane of the 20th century was in 1987. Winds of over 160kph swept across the southern counties and felled millions of trees. Modern weather forecasts, using data from satellites, has made it possible to give warning of hurricanes. This can save lives, though it cannot stop damage to buildings.

1. _____

2. _____

3. _____

4. _____

Illustrations © Theresa Tibbetts/Beehive Illustration.

Dear helper
Objective: To identify the main points in an information passage.
Task: Read the passage with your child and help them to pick out four key points. These should be the four most important facts.

Name   Date

Notes

◼ Read this encyclopedia entry about Galileo and the notes made about it.

Galileo was born in 1564 in Pisa, Italy. He was the first person to look at the night sky with a telescope. Through it he could see things that cannot be seen with the naked eye, such as the rings of Saturn and the moons of Jupiter. His book on astronomy was banned by the Church. He died in 1642.

Notes
Galileo, Italian
b. 1564
1st to use telescope
saw rings of Saturn,
moons of Jupiter
book banned by Church
d. 1642

◼ Now write your own notes for this entry about Herschel.

Herschel, Sir William, was born in 1738 in Hanover, Germany, but he spent most of his working life in England. In 1781 he discovered Uranus and some of its moons. He also discovered double stars and infra-red rays from the sun. He died in 1822.

Notes

NON-FICTION

Dear helper
Objective: To practise note-making.
Task: Help your child to study the sample notes on Galileo. They should note how only the most important points are jotted down. They should then make similar notes on Herschel.

Name	Date

NON-FICTION

TV report

◾ Watch a TV programme that is presenting information, and complete the tasks below.

Title of programme _____

◾ Tick any of these features that you notice.

Captions or subtitles		Artists' illustrations	
Still photos		Voiceover	
Music		Sound effects	
Filmed images		Interviews	
Diagrams or maps		Book or newspaper extracts	

◾ Write any words you heard or saw that were new for you.

_____

_____

_____

◾ Now write three or four sentences about the key facts in the programme.

_____

_____

_____

_____

Dear helper
Objective: To identify the features and key points in a broadcast.
Task: Help your child to choose a suitable programme, perhaps one on wildlife. Help them to spot, and spell, new vocabulary, and discuss what the words mean. The boxes can be ticked while watching the programme, but the sentences should be written afterwards.

Name	Date

Crabs

■ Read this passage about crabs. Highlight five facts that you think are important. Then rewrite your five facts in one paragraph below.

Crabs are related to lobsters and shrimps. They have five pairs of legs, the first pair having claws. The other four pairs are used for walking, which most crabs do by moving sideways. Most crabs have hard shells, though the Hermit Crab does not grow a shell of its own. It has to find one on the seabed.

Crabs come in all sizes. The smallest are Pea Crabs, which are like tiny insects. The largest are Japanese Spider Crabs, which may measure up to 3.5 metres from tip to tip of their outstretched claws.

Some types of crab eat vegetables and some catch live animals, but most crabs find their food by scavenging, in other words by searching around for scraps of dead or decaying matter.

Crabs lay eggs, and their young have to shed their shell every time they get larger and grow a new one. Crabs live between 3 and 12 years.

Illustrations © Theresa Tibbetts/Beehive Illustration.

Dear helper
Objective: To summarise in writing the content of a passage or text.
Task: The hardest part is deciding which five facts to choose. Help your child to choose five of the most important that are well spread out through the passage.

Name   Date

NON-FICTION

Animals of the Arctic

■ Cut out and rearrange the following sentences so that they make a report that is organised in a logical way.

These migrating animals are travelling north to find food and give birth to their young in the long Arctic summer.	For example, the bowhead whale, the long-tusked narwhal, and birds such as bar-tailed godwits and snow geese travel thousands of miles, while herds of caribou trudge just a few hundred.
Polar bears, musk oxen, Arctic wolves and foxes manage to survive the extreme cold of the long, dark Arctic night.	When the summer is almost over and the six-month Arctic night begins, the migrating animals start their long journeys home.
While they are there, the sun shines night and day, helping plants to bloom across the Arctic tundra.	These plants provide food for insects and small creatures, which then become food for bigger animals.
However, there are other animals living in many different parts of the world who migrate to the Arctic every year.	
This food chain means that all the animals have enough to eat and raise their young.	
Even though the Arctic is extremely cold, some animals can live there all year round.	

Illustrations © Theresa Tibbetts/Beehive Illustration.

Dear helper
Objective: To organise information logically in the form of a report.
Task: When your child has cut out the sentences, help them use both the information and the sentence openings to put them into a sensible order. Then stick them on to another sheet of paper in the order you have chosen together. Finally read through the report to check that it makes sense.

CORE SKILLS

Enjoyable, delightful, childlike

■ Turn the **nouns** and **verbs** in the first column into **adjectives** by adding one of the following **suffixes**: **-able**, **-ful**, **-like**.

Note: Most words add the suffix without change. Take care with **beauty** and **love**.

Noun or verb	Adjective
arm	armful
beauty	
break	
business	
change	
colour	
comfort	
doubt	
drink	
ear	
help	
joy	
lady	
life	
like	
love	
power	
read	
success	
war	

Illustrations © Garry Davies.

Dear helper
Objective: To explore word endings that turn nouns and verbs into adjectives: '-able', '-ful', '-like'.
Task: Help your child add the appropriate suffix. Generally, this is simply a matter of common sense, of what sounds right.

Shocking, dynamic, newsworthy!

■ Turn the **nouns** and **verbs** in the first column into **adjectives** by adding one of the following **suffixes**: **-ing**, **-ic**, **-worthy**.

Note: Some words add the suffix without change, others drop the final **e**.

Noun or verb	Adjective
ache	aching
adore	
agonise	
air	
alcohol	
artist	
astonish	
bawl	
blaze	
bleed	
boil	
bore	
cube	
enthusiast	
hero	
idiot	
magnet	
praise	
sea	
telescope	

Illustrations © Garry Davies.

Dear helper
Objective: To explore word endings that turn nouns and verbs into adjectives: '-ing', '-ic', '-worthy'.
Task: Help your child add the appropriate suffix. Generally, this is simply a matter of common sense, of what sounds right – but take care with words ending in 'e'!

Name	Date

Instructions

- Instructions serve many purposes. Look at these examples and write down what they are for.
- Collect more examples.

Micklebring 2   Braithwell 4

Clifton 1

GIVE WAY

SAFETY NOTICE

If you hear seven short blasts on the ship's whistle you must go to the nearest MUSTER STATION.
You will be given a lifejacket and told what to do next.

YUMMY-TUMMY
YELLOW CUSTARD

How to cook
Remove the foil lid and place in a microwave oven.
Cook for 3 minutes on FULL power.

WARNING! The custard will be very hot after cooking.
Allow to cool a little before serving.
Best before 10/10/10

Illustrations © Theresa Tibbetts/Beehive Illustration.

Dear helper
Objective: To identify the different purposes of instructional texts.
Task: Help your child to find more examples of instructions – the house is probably full of them. For example, instructions for electrical appliances and cooking instructions on packets and in recipe books.

NON-FICTION

Name   Date

How to make a book

■ Follow these instructions to make a 16-page mini-book.

You will need:
- ☐ A sheet of A4 paper
- ☐ A pair of scissors
- ☐ A stapler

What to do:

1. Take the sheet of A4 paper and fold in half, short side to short side.

2. Turn sideways so that the fold is at the top, then fold in half again as above.

3. Repeat step 2.

4. Turn the paper so that the all the folds are at the top and at the right-hand side.

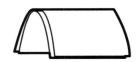

5. Open out the paper once and staple through the fold.

staple

6. Cut the folds along the top and along the right-hand side.

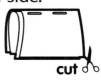

cut

Your book is finished! Now you could write a story or a collection of poems to fill it.

Illustrations © Theresa Tibbetts/Beehive Illustration.

Dear helper
Objective: To read and follow simple instructions.
Task: Read through these instructions with your child, then supervise as they follow them. They are not expected, at this stage, to write a story or collection of poems!

Name   Date

New mini-system

■ Read these instructions and highlight the following features: lists, numbered points, diagrams and bullet points.

WARNING!
To prevent fire or shock hazard,
do not expose the unit to rain or moisture.

Your retro 70s mini-system includes:

☐ 1 system box with CD player, cassette deck, radio and amplifier
☐ 2 teak-effect front speakers
☐ 4 speaker cables
☐ AM/FM antenna
☐ 1 remote control (and batteries)

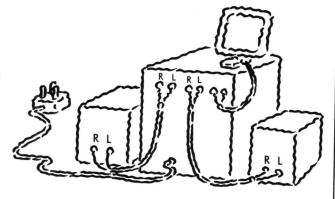

Setting up the system

1. Connect the speakers by placing the red wire in the red socket and the black wire in the black socket and closing the clips.
2. Connect the AM/FM antenna by placing the black wires in the black sockets and closing the clips.
3. Place the batteries in the remote control unit.

This mini-system has Dolby* B noise reduction.
* Dolby and the double-D symbol are trademarks of Dolby Laboratories Licensing Corporation.

Illustrations © Theresa Tibbetts/Beehive Illustration.

NON-FICTION

Dear helper
Objective: To explore how written instructions are organised.
Task: Help your child to find the features listed in the note at the top of the page. If possible, do the same with a real instruction manual.

Name   Date

NON-FICTION

Hide and seek

■ Underline all the things you can find that make this set of instructions clear, and add a few words nearby to say what these features are.

How to play hide and seek
What you need
At least two players

A playing area where there are lots of safe places to hide

What you do
1. Decide which player is going to be the seeker.
2. Agree how high the seeker will count while the other players are hiding.
3. Next, the seeker covers their eyes and counts loudly up to the agreed number.
4. While the seeker is counting, the other players quickly find a safe place to hide.
5. When the seeker has finished counting, they call 'Coming!' loudly, so that everyone should be able to hear.
6. Hiders should stay as quiet and still as possible.
7. When the seeker finds a hider, they must go back to the home base and wait until everyone has been found.
8. Finally, when everyone is at the home base, a new seeker is chosen and the game begins again.

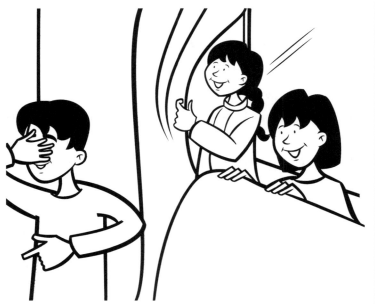

Illustrations © Theresa Tibbetts/Beehive Illustration.

Dear helper
Objective: To analyse a set of instructions and identify features of organisation and layout.
Task: Read through the instructions with your child, then decide together on the various features that help to make the instructions clear. Help them to briefly annotate the features they identify, such as *Heading, so you know what it's about*, and so on.

Name   Date

Giving directions

◾ Plan how you would tell somebody the directions for getting from your house to school (if you live very close to school, you can choose another destination).

◾ Make notes below, thinking about key words you would use, and the order the directions should be in. You might want to number each part. What landmarks might you look out for?

Words you might use					
first	next	after that	then	when	before

_____

_____

_____

_____

_____

_____

_____

_____

_____

_____

_____

_____

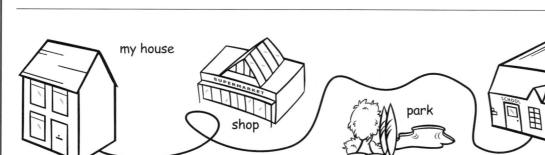

Illustrations © Theresa Tibbetts/Beehive Illustration.

NON-FICTION

Dear helper
Objective: To plan and rehearse how to give spoken instructions.
Task: Talk through the route with your child, noting names of streets, right and left turns, and any key buildings or objects you pass on the way. They do not have to write complete sentences. From their notes your child should tell you the directions.

Name   Date

NON-FICTION

What's wrong here?

▪ These instructions are not very clear. Make notes around them, saying what has been missed out and how they might be improved.

Cheesy Beans on Toast

Get some bread and toast it.

Get some beans and heat them up.

Butter the toast.

Put the beans on it.

Get some cheese.

Put it on top.

Eat it.

Illustrations © Theresa Tibbetts/Beehive Illustration.

Dear helper
Objective: To identify key features of an instruction text.
Task: Help your child to think about missing items such as numbered stages, bullet points, clearer explanations, good verb choices, extra details and so on. The space on the sheet is to make annotations and notes, not to rewrite the instructions. You could make the beans on toast to help you.

PHOTOCOPIABLE **SCHOLASTIC**
www.scholastic.co.uk

Name	Date

How to make a healthy sandwich

◼ Write instructions for making a sandwich. Choose your own healthy sandwich filling.

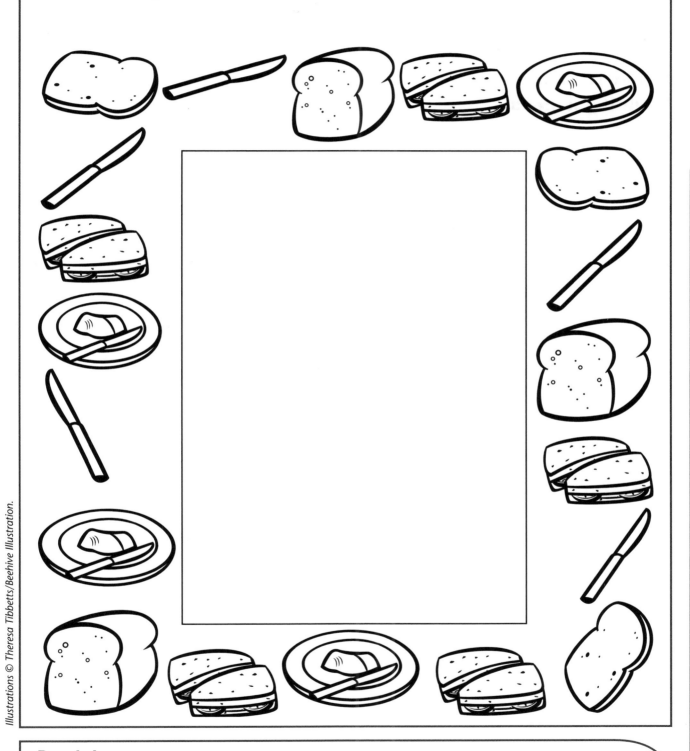

Illustrations © Theresa Tibbetts/Beehive Illustration.

NON-FICTION

Dear helper
Objective: To write a set of instructions for making something.
Task: Help your child to choose a sandwich. If possible, make it before writing the instructions. Extra bullet points or numbers can be added if they are needed, using the other side of this page.

Name   Date

NON-FICTION

How do you do it?

◼ Watch a children's TV programme, or a cooking show where someone is showing you how to make something. You might want to make some notes while you watch. Then write your own instructions to explain to someone else how to make it.

How to make _____

What you need

_____

_____

_____

_____

_____

_____

What you do

1. _____

_____

2. _____

_____

3. _____

_____

4. _____

_____

5. _____

_____

Dear helper
Objective: To write a set of instructions for making something.
Task: Reassure your child that their instructions need only be simple, so help them to choose something appropriate to explain. Help as they make notes, and ask what they think are the key points to include.

PHOTOCOPIABLE ⬛SCHOLASTIC
www.scholastic.co.uk

'SS'

- Add **s** or **ss** to each of the following words. Take particular care with the last three words in the right-hand column.
- Find more words containing the letter sequence **ss**.

CORE SKILLS

le____on

ab____ence   po____ible   ki____

proce____   mini____ter   a____thma

succe____   mi____ile   Ru____ian

se____ion   a____cend   a____e____

ob____tacle   gue____   di____cu____ion

Al____ation   a____teroid   po____e____ion

                    goodne____

Dear helper

Objective: To explore the letter sequence 'ss'.

Task: The letter sequence 'ss' causes spelling problems in some words, particularly words like the last three in the right-hand column. Encourage your child to consult a dictionary where necessary.

CORE SKILLS

Possible... and probable!

The endings of **-ible** and **-able** words are often confused because they sound so similar.

Tip: When learning the spellings of these words, emphasise the ending:
horr – ible (say ibble)
ador – able (say abble)

- Look at the cards below and learn which ending goes with which words.
- Cut up the cards, mix them up, and try to put the words back together with the correct ending.
- Make more cards by finding other words with these endings.

ed	ible	ador	able
horr	ible	break	able
indestruct	ible	dispos	able
invince	ible	enjoy	able
poss	ible	miser	able
respons	ible	prob	able
revers	ible	reli	able
terr	ible	valu	able

Illustrations © Garry Davies.

Dear helper
Objective: To recognise and spell suffixes: '-ible', '-able'.
Task: When your child makes a correct pair, remove it from the game so that the focus is on words they still need to learn. When they have mastered the above, help them to find other words to make extra cards.

Looking for a misplaced exit?

■ Find three more words that start with each of the prefixes below. You can use a dictionary to help you. Then use Look, Say, Cover, Write, Check to learn how to spell all 12 words.

Look, Say, Cover	Write and Check 1	Write and Check 2
Words starting with the prefix **mis-** (meaning 'wrong')		
misplace		
Words starting with the prefix **non-** (meaning 'not')		
non-stick		
Words starting with the prefix **ex-** (meaning 'out' or 'outside of')		
exit		

Dear helper
Objective: To learn to spell words starting with the prefixes 'mis-', 'non-', 'ex-'.
Task: Help your child to choose words that will be useful, and that they can read. Having two attempts at spelling the words will help to reinforce them.

Name   Date

NON-FICTION

King Arthur

■ Compare and discuss these two information texts.

KING ARTHUR ON THE WEB

Welcome to the King Arthur website. Here you will find everything you need to know about Britain's legendary hero. Just click on an icon.

 The legend

 Historical facts

 Archaeology

 Pictures of Arthur

 Clips from films about Arthur

 Links

THE LEGEND OF ARTHUR

In the 5th century AD, Britain was invaded by Anglo-Saxons. The Britons fought back, and legend tells us that they were led by someone called Arthur. However, the Arthur of history would not have worn shining armour or lived in a huge castle. He would have worn the simple dress of a Celt and lived in a hill fort.

Illustrations © Theresa Tibbetts/Beehive Illustration.

Dear helper
Objective: To compare a variety of information texts including computer-based sources.
Task: Read these two texts with your child and discuss them. Both show only the beginnings. Ask: *What would come next? How would the reader of the book find information on other aspects of King Arthur? What are the advantages and disadvantages of each type of information source?*

Name	Date

Seaside index

An **index** is a detailed alphabetical list of all the topics in a book.

- ▢ People's names are written with the last name first.
- ▢ Articles such as **a** and **the** are written after the main word.
- ▢ When a range of pages is listed, for example **5–7**, this is the place where the most information about a topic can be found.

◼ Look at the index and time yourself on the tasks below (answer them on the back of this sheet).

◼ Then ask your helper to ask you other, similar, questions.

A
Antarctica 2, 5, 18, 20,
　　　　　　30–1
Arctic, the 31
arctic tern 32

B
barnacle 15
blenny 19
Bounty, The 23
butterfish 17

C
clam 12, 15
Cook, Captain James 27
coral 25
crab 8, 9–11, 28
Crusoe, Robinson 26

E
eel 2, 5–6
eskimo 4, 30

F
fish 17, 19–21, 29
flatfish 19
flounder 20
fossil 18, 30

L
limpet 23
lobster 5
lugworm 21

P
pearl 3, 7
penguin 31
polar bear 32
puffin 30

R
razorbill 14
rockling 22
rockpool 7, 9, 29

S
sand dunes 15
scallop 9
sea anemone 24
seals 8
seaweed 31
Scott, Robert F 27, 30
shell 4, 11, 22
shingle 5
starfish 11

1. Where would you look to find out about polar bears?
2. In which pages would you find most information about fish?
3. Which page gives information about Captain Cook?
4. Which page gives information about the ship *The Bounty*?
5. Which topic does the book give most information on?

Illustrations © Theresa Tibbetts/Beehive Illustration.

Dear helper
Objective: To scan an index to locate information quickly and accurately.
Task: Time your child as they scan the index to answer the questions. Ask a range of similar questions. If available, use a real reference book and time how long it takes to find each page and place.

NON-FICTION

Name   Date

NON-FICTION

Be a librarian

◾ This shelf of books is waiting to be classified. Write the Dewey Decimal system set number on each one.

Set number	Group name	What the books are about
000-099	General works	Many different subjects
100-199	Philosophy	People's thoughts and their ways of thinking
200-299	Religion	People's ideas about God
300-399	Social sciences	How people live together
400-499	Language	How people talk to each other
500-599	Pure science	Nature, the world and the universe
600-699	Technology	Ways to use science to help us
700-799	The arts	Painting, music, dancing, sports and games
800-899	Literature	Stories and poetry
900-999	History, geography, biography	People, places and important events

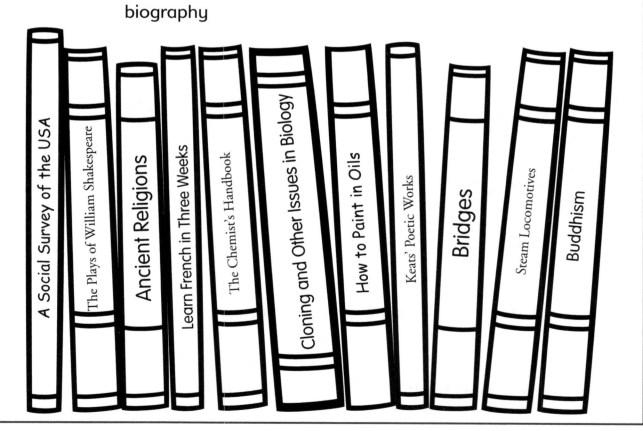

A Social Survey of the USA · The Plays of William Shakespeare · Ancient Religions · Learn French in Three Weeks · The Chemist's Handbook · Cloning and Other Issues in Biology · How to Paint in Oils · Keats' Poetic Works · Bridges · Steam Locomotives · Buddhism

Illustrations © Theresa Tibbetts/Beehive Illustration.

Dear helper
Objective: To locate books by classification.
Task: Help your child to classify these books. If you have a suitable collection, try classifying some of them.

Name	Date

My favourite things

■ Think of something that you are particularly interested in, and that you would like to find out more about. Answer the questions below about how you would find more information and how you would present the information to others.

What would you like to find out more about? _____

What are some of the things you would like to know?

_____

_____

_____

Which of these places might you be able to find the information? (Tick any boxes that you would find helpful.)

non-fiction books ▢   the internet ▢   CD-ROM ▢

an adult ▢   a friend ▢   magazine ▢

Anywhere else? _____

When you have found your information, how would you present it for others? (Tick one.)

story ▢   poem ▢   book ▢

poster ▢   computer presentation ▢   web page ▢

leaflet ▢   spoken presentation ▢   explanation ▢

Anything else? _____

Why do you think what you have chosen would work best for your information?

_____

Dear helper
Objective: To identify how to find information from a variety of sources, and present it to others.
Task: Talk with your child about what they would choose, and ask them to explain their choices when ticking the boxes.

NON-FICTION

Name

Date

Buy it now!

■ Choose an advert from a newspaper, magazine or junk mail that is trying to sell you something. See how many of the features on the grid below you can find on your chosen advert.

Feature	Tick if you see it	Give some details
Photograph		
Single, eye-catching words		
Exclamation or question marks		
Some words in big or bold writing		
Bright colours		
Clever information		

■ Write here any words you think have been used to persuade you to buy the product.

_____

_____

_____

Dear helper
Objective: To identify the features of a persuasive text.
Task: Help your child to choose a suitable advert; one that they have some interest in, and talk about the features you can identify. The details need only be brief, such as *happy child playing with toy* for the photograph, or *scientific words* for clever information and so on. They should take the advert back to school with this sheet.

NON-FICTION

Name   Date

TV adverts

▪ While you are watching TV, make notes of some of the persuasive words that are used in the adverts between the programmes, then complete the grid below.

Time of day and channel	Programme on before the advert	What is being advertised?	Persuasive words

▪ Which words do you think are the most persuasive?

_____

_____

Dear helper
Objective: To identify persuasive language in a TV advert.
Task: This grid can be filled in over several days, and will be more interesting if the viewing is done at slightly different times, and perhaps on a variety of channels. Help your child to spot the persuasive words if they are finding it difficult.

NON-FICTION

Name   Date

Wear your helmet!

■ An important aspect of road safety is for cyclists to wear safety helmets. But some people still don't do this. Design a poster to persuade cyclists to wear their safety helmets. Think about:

Eye-catching words   Persuasive language   Clear illustrations   Colours

NON-FICTION

Dear helper
Objective: To use the features of a persuasive text to design a poster.
Task: Talk with your child about what they know of the features of persuasive texts. Encourage them to keep the poster clear and simple, with a few well-chosen words.

Name   Date

Good idea, bad idea

■ For each of the statements below, write two or three persuasive arguments against them.

Motorists should be able to drive on whichever side of the road they want.
No, that is not a good idea because...

_____

_____

_____

Children should be able to eat sweets at school.
No, that is not a good idea because...

_____

_____

_____

People should be able to keep wild animals as pets.
No, that is not a good idea because...

_____

_____

_____

Children should not do PE at school. They should all join sports clubs instead.
No, that is not a good idea because...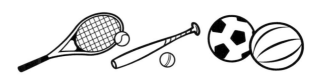

_____

_____

_____

Dear helper
Objective: To use the language of persuasion in a given context.
Task: Discuss the statements with your child, encouraging them to think of good arguments against them. If they are finding it difficult, try asking them questions, such as *What would happen if...?*

■SCHOLASTIC PHOTOCOPIABLE
www.scholastic.co.uk

Illustrations © Theresa Tibbetts/Beehive Illustration.

NON-FICTION

Name   Date

Safely to school

◼ Imagine that there is a need for a pedestrian-controlled crossing near your school, and the children have decided to write to the local council to ask if one could be installed.

◼ Write a draft letter below, trying your best to persuade them why the crossing would be a good thing. Try to write in paragraphs.

◼ Think about: good reasons, persuasive language, use of questions.

Illustrations © Theresa Tibbetts/Beehive Illustration.

Dear helper
Objective: To use persuasive language in a letter.
Task: Help your child to think of good reasons for installing the crossing – you could make a list on the back of this sheet. Remind them to use persuasive words and phrases as well as thinking of good questions that might persuade them.

Grace Darling

A **connective** is a joining word. It joins parts of a sentence together.
For example: Grace got in the boat **and** began to row.

Some common conjunctions are:

and   if   so   while   though   since   when

■ Read this true story about Grace Darling. Choose one of the
conjunctions above to put in each gap below. You may use each
conjunction in the list only once.

On the morning of September 7, 1838, the steamer *Forfarshire* was caught

in a storm _____ she was on her way to Liverpool. She hit

a rock _____ began to sink. No other lifeboat dared to risk

the storm _____ Grace and her father, William, put to sea in

a small boat. They managed to reach the wreck, _____ they

could only rescue five people in their small boat. _____

they reached the shore, William, helped by two of the men, went to

save the four others. However, _____ Grace had not been

brave enough to help her father on the first trip, all nine people would

have drowned. For her bravery, Grace was awarded a Gold Medal,

and so many people requested locks of her hair that she joked that

she had been almost bald _____ the rescue!

Dear helper
Objective: To join sentences using connectives.
Task: Read through this story with your child and discuss the most appropriate connectives for each gap.

Illustrations © Theresa Tibbetts/Beehive Illustration.

CORE SKILLS

Time sequence

■ Choose one of the words and phrases showing time sequence to fill each gap in the text below. You may use each word or phrase once only.

a long time   after   again   first   in the end   not long   one day   when   at last

_____ in 1066, Duke William landed at Hastings.

The _____

_____ thing he did was to order his cavalry to charge.

But the English axemen held them off for

_____.

_____ they weakened and fled.

_____ the English saw this they ran after them.

But it was _____

_____ before they were surrounded and killed.

_____ this disaster, the English were badly weakened.

So the Normans attacked

_____.

King Harold was hit in the eye by an arrow. The battle was lost.

■ Think of more words that show time sequence and make a list of them.

Illustrations © Theresa Tibbetts/Beehive Illustration.

Dear helper
Objective: To investigate how words and phrases can signal time sequences.
Task: Help your child by checking that the words chosen to fill the gaps are appropriate. Help them to think of more time sequence words. Try looking in books, magazines and newspapers at home.

Commotion and confusion

The endings of **-tion** and **-sion** words are often confused because both are pronounced **-shun**.

- Look at the cards and learn which ending goes with which words.
- Cut up the cards, mix them up, and try to put the words back together with the correct ending.
- Make more cards by finding other words with these endings.

addi	tion	conclu	sion
commo	tion	confu	sion
direc	tion	deci	sion
educa	tion	divi	sion
imagina	tion	explo	sion
punctua	tion	exten	sion
tempta	tion	supervi	sion
varia	tion	televi	sion

Illustrations © Garry Davies.

Dear helper
Objective: To recognise and spell suffixes: '-tion', '-sion'.
Task: When your child makes a correct pair, remove it from the game so that the focus is on words they still need to learn. When they have mastered the above, help them to find other words to make extra cards.

Name	Date

Text © 1984, James Berry; illustrations © Theresa Tibbetts/Beehive Illustration.

Dialogue Between Two Large Village Women

■ Read this poem and perform it with a partner or your helper.

Vergie mi gal, yu know
wha overtek me?

      Wha, Bet-Bet darlin?

Yu know de downgrow buoy
dey call Runt?

      Everybody know de lickle
      orceripe wretch.

Well mi dear, de bwoy put
question to mi.

      Wha? Wha yu sey?

Yeahs – put question to mi
big-big woman, who could be
him mummah over and over.

      Laad above. Didn yu bounce
      de lickle ramgoat face?

Mi hol him an mi shake
de lickle beas like
to kill de wretch.
An yu know wha happen?

      No.

De lickle brute try fi kiss mi.

from Caribbean Poetry Now *by James Berry*

Dear helper
Objective: To choose and prepare a poem for performance.
Task: Help your child with the phonetic pronunciation of the words, then take each part in turn.

Name	Date

Why?

🔳 Perform this poem with another person. Then, on a separate sheet, add more verses following the same pattern. A good place to add the new verses would be before the last two lines.

🔳 Try to write a completely new Why? poem, using the same pattern.

I'm just going out for a moment

I'm just going out for a moment.
Why?
To make a cup of tea.
Why?
Because I'm thirsty.
Why?
Because it's hot.
Why?
Because the sun is shining.
Why?
Because it's summer.
Why?
Because that's when it is.
Why?
Why don't you stop saying why?
Why?

from Wouldn't you like to know *by Michael Rosen*

Text © 1977, Michael Rosen; illustrations © Theresa Tibbetts/Beehive Illustration.

POETRY

Dear helper
Objective: To write new verses for a given poem, following the same pattern.
Task: Perform this poem with your child, then think of ideas for new verses. Help your child to write a whole new poem on the same pattern.

Name	Date

Overheard on a Saltmarsh

■ Read this poem aloud, then plan a performance of it.

Nymph, nymph, what are your beads?

Green glass, goblin. Why do you stare at them?

Give them me.

        No.

Give them me. Give them me.

        No.

Then I will howl all night in the reeds,

Lie in the mud and howl for them.

Goblin, why do you love them so?

They are better than stars or water,

Better than voices of winds that sing,

Better than any man's fair daughter,

Your green glass beads on a silver ring.

Hush I stole them out of the moon.

Give me your beads, I desire them.

        No.

I will howl in a deep lagoon

For your green glass beads, I love them so.

Give them me. Give them.

        No.

From Collected Poems *by Harold Monro*

Text © 1970, Harold Monro; illustrations © Phil Garner.

Dear helper

Objective: To read and plan to perform a poem.

Task: Read the poem with your child and talk about how it involves two characters who have a dialogue. Help your child to plan a performance. This could include simple movements, for example crouching to suggest a goblin. Encourage your child to use a realistic tone of voice.

POETRY

Name	Date

Shape up!

A **calligram** is a word or poem that is written in a way that shows its meaning. Here is an example:

Friendly Warning

LISTEN GRASS, TAKE
IT EASY. DON'T GROW
TOO TALL. THEY'LL JUST
BRING IN A LAWN
MOWER AND CUT
YOU DOWN   SHORT.
SEE? I TOLD YOU THEY WOULD.

From Seeing Things *by Robert Froman*

A **shape poem** is a poem in which the words are set out in a shape that fits the meaning of the words. Here is an example:

Mosquito

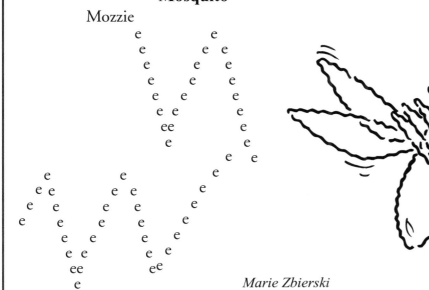

Marie Zbierski

◼ On a separate piece of paper, try some calligrams and shape poems for yourself.

Friendly warnings © 1974, Robert Froman; Mosquito © Marie Zbierski; illustrations © Theresa Tibbetts/ Beehive Illustration.

Dear helper
Objective: To invent calligrams and a range of shape poems.
Task: Have fun helping your child to invent calligrams and shape poems!

Name   Date

Shape poems

◼ Read the poems and make some notes about how they are different from each other.

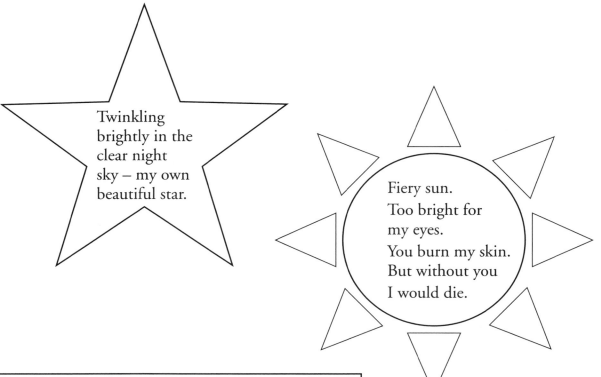

Twinkling brightly in the clear night sky – my own beautiful star.

Fiery sun.
Too bright for my eyes.
You burn my skin.
But without you I would die.

POETRY

Calligrams

The light from the bonfire

sparkles, and a rocket

EXPLODES! into the sky.

What will happen when the

Beautiful

princess finally comes face to face with the

Monster?

Dear helper
Objective: To compare calligrams and shape poems.
Task: Help your child to see how these two types of poems differ, and practise reading them out loud.

PHOTOCOPIABLE ▨ SCHOLASTIC
www.scholastic.co.uk

Name	Date

Comparing poems

■ Compare two poems on the same subject by filling in this table.

	Title:	**Title:**
	Poet:	**Poet:**
Subject (Explain in your own words what the poem says.)		
Verse form (Is it written in rhyming or non-rhyming verse? If it is in rhyming verse, what is the pattern of rhymes?)		
Interesting words and phrases (Jot down any interesting words or phrases and say why you chose them.)		
Opinion (Which of the two poems do you like best? Why?)		

POETRY

Dear helper
Objective: To compare two poems on the same subject.
Task: Your child will have been given two poems to compare. Read them together. Help your child to fill in the table by discussing both poems and helping your child to pick out illustrative words and phrases.

Name	Date

Spider spider

▪ Create your own shape poem in the spider shape below. Think about: nouns that match the subject, good adjectives, similes, descriptive phrases.

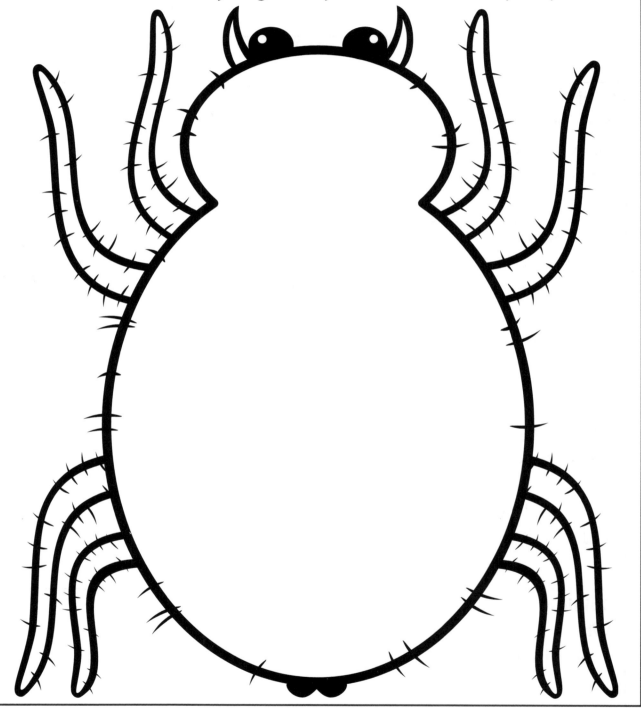

Illustrations © Theresa Tibbetts/Beehive Illustration.

Dear helper
Objective: To create a shape poem.
Task: Remind your child that shape poems are inspired by the shape of the object that the poem is about. Help them to think of appropriate words using the bullet points, and put them into thoughts, ideas and descriptions of the spider.

PHOTOCOPIABLE ▬SCHOLASTIC
www.scholastic.co.uk

POETRY

Abstract nouns

An **abstract noun** names a concept or idea rather than a specific thing:

Examples: **jealousy, love, motherhood**

The suffixes **-ship**, **-hood** and **-ness** can be added to certain nouns and adjectives to make them abstract nouns:

Examples: **father** + hood = **fatherhood**   **author** + ship = **authorship**

         cold + ness = **coldness**

The suffixes can be added to most words without changing the spelling, but note that, words ending in **y** change the **y** to **i** before adding a suffix:

Example: **lazy** + ness = **laziness**

■ Add the appropriate suffix (**-ship**, **-hood** or **-ness**) to the following nouns or adjectives to make abstract nouns. The first one has been done for you.

Noun or adjective	Abstract noun
author	authorship
awkward	
bitter	
blind	
bright	
busy	
cheerful	
child	
citizen	
false	
friend	
happy	
hard	
knight	
leader	
likely	
man	
relation	
woman	

Dear helper

Objective: To make abstract nouns using the suffixes: '-ship', '-hood', '-ness'.

Task: Read through the list of words with your child. They should be able to choose the correct suffix through association, but help may be needed with some words.

Illustrations © Garry Davies.

CORE SKILLS

Name	Date

Cats!

■ Here's a poem that has fun playing with words, to describe all kinds of cats. Read it through, and underline all the words that have been invented to describe some of the cats. Then practise reading it aloud, imagining the different cats as you do so.

Cats!

Cats!

We're cats!

Lankies and skinnies and scruffies and fats;

Cats of all colours and cats of all sizes;

Nosers in dustbins and winners of prizes;

Loungers on shelfers and scratchers of fleasers;

Long hairies, short hairies, chewed earers, proud tailers;

Mewers and purrers and spitters and wailers;

Burmese and Siamese, Persian and *Manx* cats,

Marmalades, *Tabbies,* Chinchillas and Van Cats;

Strutters and sidlers and nuzzlers and liers;

Starers through windows and lazers near firers;

Chasers of mousies and catchers of rats;

We're cats!

Cats!

Anon.

Illustrations © Theresa Tibbetts/ Beehive Illustration.

POETRY

Dear helper
Objective: To identify language that plays with words, and practise reading a poem for performance.
Task: Help your child to read the poem and identify the made-up words, discussing what they mean. Look out for the names for different breeds of cat. Read the poem aloud together until your child is confident enough to read it on their own.

Name   Date

Moths and Moonshine

Alliteration is often used in poetry and advertisements as a special effect. It occurs when words close together begin with the same sound:

Sing a **S**ong of **S**ixpence...
Budget **b**rown **b**read **b**eats the **b**lues!

◗ Read this poem, then highlight all the letters that alliterate.

Moths and Moonshine

Moths and moonshine mean to me
Magic – madness – mystery.

Witches dancing weird and wild
Mischief make for man and child.

Owls screech from woodland shades,
Moths glide through moonlit glades,

Moving in dark and secret wise
Like a plotter in disguise.

Moths and moonshine mean to me
Magic – madness – mystery.

From Complete poems for children *by James Reeves*

◗ Now write your own short poem that uses alliteration.

_____

_____

_____

_____

POETRY

Dear helper
Objective: To write poetry that uses alliteration to create effects.
Task: Read this poem aloud with your child. You could take the verses in turn. Encourage your child to listen carefully for the effect of the alliteration and then to highlight or underline all the letter sounds that alliterate in the poem. Finally, help your child to write a short alliterative poem of their own.

Name	Date

Playing with rhymes

■ Have fun changing the following nursery rhymes. An example has been given to help you.

The Grand Old Duke of York

He had ten thousand pens

He wrote until they all ran out

Then he filled them up again.

■ Now change these rhymes. Write your new version on the back of this sheet.

Jack and Jill went up the hill

To fetch a pail of water.

Jack fell down and broke his crown

And Jill came tumbling after.

Humpty Dumpty sat on a wall

Humpty Dumpty had a great fall

All the king's horses and all the king's men

Couldn't put Humpty together again.

Little Bo-Peep has lost her sheep

And doesn't know where to find them

Leave them alone and they'll come home

Wagging their tails behind them.

Illustrations © Theresa Tibbetts/ Beehive Illustration.

Dear helper
Objective: To use a known rhyme as the basis for writing a new one.
Task: Help your child to have fun creating new versions of these well-known rhymes. Read the new rhymes together.

PHOTOCOPIABLE 📖 **SCHOLASTIC**
www.scholastic.co.uk

Name	Date

Create-a-poem

■ Fill in the grid below to see what words you create. Some have been done to show you how it works. Most will be nonsense words.

	oat	ing	ash
sp			
cr		cring	
pl			
ch	choat		

■ Use the words to create some short nonsense rhyming poems. Here's an example:

The old shiny cring

Sat weeping one day

He'd lost his best sping

When he went out to play.

Illustrations © Theresa Tibbetts/ Beehive Illustration.

Dear helper
Objective: To write a rhyming nonsense poem.
Task: The poems your child will write are similar to those of Edward Lear, so you may like to track some down to read together. Help your child with starting lines for their poems if they get stuck for ideas.

POETRY

Name	Date

Word play

◼ Read and enjoy these poems, then highlight the words that are 'played' with by the poet.

Away from it all © 1939, Ogden Nash; Little Spider © 1972, Mervyn Peake; illustrations © Phil Garner.

POETRY

Away From It All
I wish I were a Tibetan monk
Living in a monastery.
I would unpack my trunk
And store it in a tronastery;
I would collect all my junk
And send it to a jonastery;
I would try to reform a drunk,
And pay his expenses at a dronastery
If my income shrunk
I would send it to a shronastery.
From Candy is Dandy *by Ogden Nash*

Little Spider
Little Spider
spider sadly
in the webly
light of leaves!
Why deride a
spider's mentadly
when it's hebly
full of grieves?

Little spider
legged and
lonely in the
bony way of
thieves. Where's
the fly-da
on the phonebly?
*From A Book of Nonsense
by Mervyn Peake*

The ankle's chief end is exposiery
Of the latest designs in silk hosiery;
    Also, I suspect,
    It's a means to connect
The part called the calf with the toesiery.
Anon

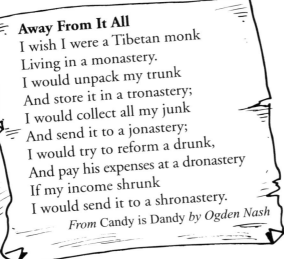

There were three ghostesses
Sitting on postesses
Eating buttered toastesses
And greasing their fistesses
Right up to their wristesses,
Weren't they beastesses
To make such feastesses!
Anon

Dear helper
Objective: To investigate how poets achieve humour through word play.
Task: Take it in turns with your child to read the poems and then talk about how each plays with words.

A gaggle of geese

A **collective noun** names a group of people or things: **a gaggle** of geese.

◤ Join each collective noun to the correct group of people or things.
One has been done for you.

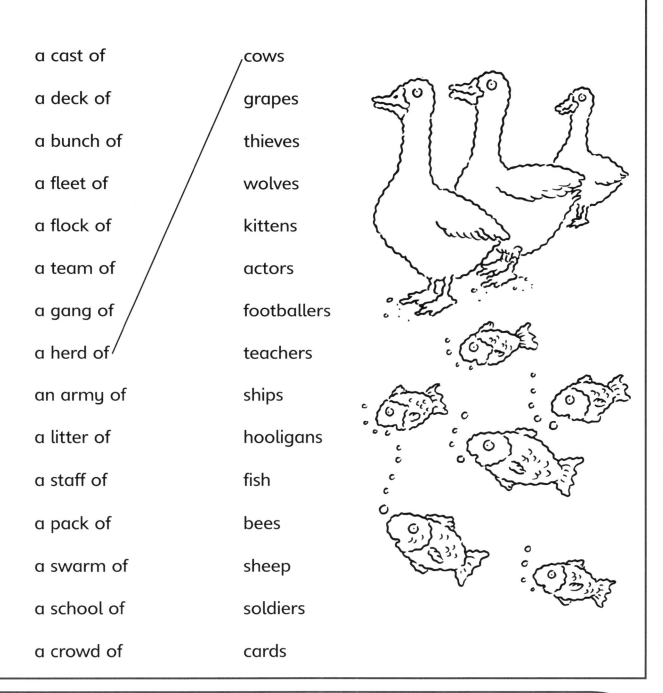

a cast of	cows
a deck of	grapes
a bunch of	thieves
a fleet of	wolves
a flock of	kittens
a team of	actors
a gang of	footballers
a herd of	teachers
an army of	ships
a litter of	hooligans
a staff of	fish
a pack of	bees
a swarm of	sheep
a school of	soldiers
a crowd of	cards

Illustrations © Theresa Tibbetts/ Beehive Illustration.

CORE SKILLS

Dear helper
Objective: To understand what a collective noun is and to match collective nouns to their appropriate nouns.
Task: Some of these collective nouns will be known to your child. Some may require your help. Encourage your child to make a guess and to use a dictionary, if one is available.

SCHOLASTIC

Also available in this series:

ISBN 978-1407-10115-6

ISBN 978-1407-10116-3

ISBN 978-1407-10117-0

ISBN 978-1407-10118-7

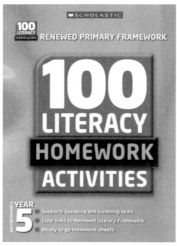

ISBN 978-1407-10119-4

ISBN 978-1407-10120-0

To find out more, call: 0845 603 9091
or visit our website www.scholastic.co.uk